LABORATORY MANUAL FOR PHYSIOLOGY OF EXERCISE

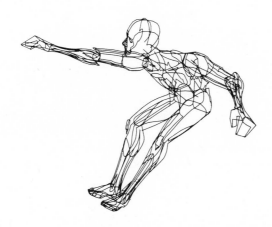

Laboratory manual
for physiology of exercise

LAURENCE E. MOREHOUSE, Ph.D.

Professor and Director of the Human Performance Laboratory,
Department of Physical Education, University of California,
Los Angeles, Calif.

With 63 illustrations

THE C. V. MOSBY COMPANY

Saint Louis 1972

Copyright © 1972 by The C. V. Mosby Company

Printed in the United States of America

International Standard Book Number 0-8016-3480-6

Distributed in Great Britain by Henry Kimpton, London

PREFACE

This laboratory manual presents physiological measurements of exercise responses in man. It is organized so that the student can make immediate use of the subject material of an exercise physiology course through action projects. Topics are keyed to two textbooks: Morehouse and Miller's *Physiology of Exercise,* ed. 6, St. Louis, 1971, The C. V. Mosby Co., and Åstrand and Rodahl's *Textbook of Work Physiology,* New York, 1970, McGraw-Hill Book Co.

Following an introduction to the special tools for laboratory studies in exercise physiology and procedures for their safe and scholarly use, each chapter contains definitions, limitations of methods, calibration and use of instruments, and step-by-step procedures and calculations. Study aids include proficiency checks, sample experiments, and data sheets. At the end of each chapter is a list of references to basic literature on laboratory methods in physiology of exercise.

Laurence E. Morehouse

CONTENTS

CHAPTER 1

INTRODUCTION

NATURE OF INQUIRY IN EXERCISE PHYSIOLOGY

The special tools for laboratory studies of exercise physiology described in this manual can be used to solve problems directly related to human health, fitness, and performance of work and sport. As examples: (1) How can exercise stress tests be used for the detection of signs of physiological deterioration early enough to enable the individual to intervene against certain diseases and disabilities? (2) How can observation of exercise responses be used to guide the individual to the best type, intensity, duration, and frequency of physical activity to achieve the specific fitness desired? (3) How can analysis of physiological costs of work and measurements of physiological fatigue from work be used to aid in job selection, planning work-rest schedules, and increasing productivity while making work easy and comfortable? (4) How can physiological conditioning for maximum performance in sport be programmed and controlled so that daily training can progress most rapidly with complete safety and avoidance of staleness?

Beyond these practical investigations the inquisitive scholar employs the laboratory and its tools to serve his quest to better understand the physiological mechanism underlying the phenomena of exercise. There are fascinating discoveries to be made: (1) Why is muscular strength increased by exercise? (2) Why does exercise increase bone density? (3) What is the mechanism by which blood volume and blood cells are altered by exercise? (4) Is heavy exercise superior to light exercise in preventing heart disease? The student is not expected to find the complete answers to questions such as these in a laboratory course, but he may well discover leading clues. The thrill of finding the first clue is no less than that of the final elucidation.

INSTRUMENTATION

There is almost no standardization of physiology of exercise instrumentation or methods, but the following groups are working toward the achievement of some uniformity:

International Biological Programme, Human Adaptability Project, Physical Fitness Sub-
   Committee
International Committee on the Standardization of Physical Fitness Tests
World Health Organization

The inclusion of an instrument in this manual is not an endorsement or an implication that it is the instrument of choice but, rather, means that the instrument is typical or demonstrates a particular point. Almost as important as an instrument itself are the operating instructions, which include usable circuit diagrams and techniques of calibration, adjustment, parts replacement, and repair. The purchaser of a new instrument does well to insist that the manufacturer include these written instructions with the delivery of the instrument.

Because of the diversity in the performance characteristics of physiology of exercise instruments, and because the physiological response is in part dependent upon these characteristics, it is important in reports of experiments to describe in detail the instrument used and its characteristics.

CHAPTER 2

PREPARATION FOR LABORATORY WORK

The presence of familiar exercise devices and sporting goods in a laboratory often invites free play and "horsing around" in informal competition. Exercise should be enjoyed, but in the physiology of exercise laboratory the devices are carefully calibrated to give accurate data; the associated precision instruments are often delicate, and some are potentially lethal.

By adopting certain regulatory procedures, work in the laboratory can progress in the orderly climate necessary for safe and scholarly investigation.

ORGANIZATION AND OPERATION OF A STUDENT LABORATORY

The following organization simulates that which is often found in a well-run research facility.

Experiment stations

Available materials and facilities are divided into a number of stations to provide work places for class subdivisions of ten or fewer team members. During one or more class periods, depending on the duration of each project, each team plans and performs an experiment, using the materials and facilities at the assigned station.

Each team is supervised by a faculty member or a laboratory assistant; teams performing uncomplicated experiments are supervised by trained student assistants.

In a typical team effort, the supervisor demonstrates the equipment at the station and discusses its use in connection with studies reported in text and lecture presentations. Members of the team then explore investigative possibilities, and a feasible experiment is developed. With the assistance of the supervisor the problem is defined, research procedures are established, and data are recorded under the experimental conditions specified. Then the data are analyzed, reported on Form 1, and discussed in detail within the team. A brief report of the studies and findings of each team is later made to the entire class.

When a team completes a project, it rotates to another station, and the process is repeated.

Student roles

As a team develops an experiment, each member of the team assumes one or more of the roles defined below.

1. *Responsible investigator.* Assigns responsibilities and directs experiment. Defines and explains the problem and method of investigation. Sees that all equipment and record sheets are ready. Supervises experiment and sees that all procedures are being properly carried out. Evaluates, writes, and reports results in manuscript form, such as that in the *Journal of Applied Physiology* or the *Style Manual for Biological Journals* (1966).
2. *Secretary.* Obtains schedules of availability of laboratory for experiments. Procures, issues, and returns equipment and supplies. Under direction of the responsible investigator, prepares instructions to subjects and other papers as needed. Solicits subjects, mails each subject instructions and follows up by telephone. Schedules appointments

---

FORM 1

Project report outline

Responsible investigator: _____

Collaborator(s): _____

Date: _____

Title of investigation: _____

Statement of problem: _____

Related publications (author, title, name of journal, volume, number, pages, date): _____

_____

Method of study

    Subjects (description, number): _____

    Measurements

        Instruments (model, manufacturer, modifications): _____

        Techniques of observation, recording, and computation (reference or description):

        _____

    Procedure (step by step): _____

Results

    Data: _____

    Analysis: _____

    Discussion: _____

    Summary: _____

                 Approved: _____

---

    in an appointment calendar. At end of testing, turns in appointment calendar to the statistician.

3. *Recorder.* Prepares master sheet for tabulation of data and keeps running record of raw or reduced data obtained at all stations.

4. *Controller.* Prepares time plan for the experiment. Calls out time intervals for each event and notes exact time of each phase in proper format for the recorder.

5. *Anthropologist.* Obtains appropriate anthropometric information (height, weight, etc.), personal data (sex, age, etc.), and history (health, exercise, etc.) from subjects in proper format for the recorder.

6. *Climatologist.* Obtains meteorological information on atmosphere of laboratory, and thermal condition of subjects in proper format for the recorder. Makes STPD or BTPS corrections of gas samples.

7. *Engineer.* Calibrates and adjusts all instruments before experiment. Controls instruments (e.g., ergometer) during experiment. Reports settings and meter readings in proper format to the recorder.

8. *Chemist.* Prepares collection equipment. Collects samples during experiment. Performs analyses. Reports results in proper format to the recorder.

9. *Safety monitor.* Checks to see that no possible harmful conditions exist—potential cause of fire, explosion, or toxicity, defective equipment, etc. Sees that rescuscitation equipment is ready and performs first aid or rescuscitation if required. Sees that emergency numbers and information are displayed at nearest telephone. Performs continuous evaluation of condition of subjects and reports poor or unusual responses to the responsible investigator. Directs emergency and rescue procedures when necessary.

10. *Photographer.* Prepares photographic equipment—camera, lights, reflectors, backdrops, ladder, etc. Performs still and/or motion picture documentation of experiment. Edits and writes legends for photographs and/or scripts for motion picture films. Presents photographic record to the responsible investigator.

11. *Statistician.* Selects formulas for reduction and analysis of data. Prepares data computation sheets. Performs statistical calculations and prepares charts, graphs, and statistical summary. Presents statistical results to the responsible investigator.

12. *Subject.* Familiarizes himself with the nature of the experiment and the potential hazards involved. Ascertains that he is fit for the test and free of contraindications for exercise. Volunteers to serve as subject. Dresses in exercise shorts (plus bra for women) and rubber-soled gym shoes and wears a washable robe or large towel for warmth. Carries out the instructions and directions of the responsible investigator. Comments on personal reactions to experimental procedures when requested by the recorder.

Every role is assigned among team members in all experiments. Early in the course each student selects those roles with which he already has some familiarity. He gains knowledge and experience in less familiar roles later in the term.

Familiarization and safety checkout

Prior to the team experimentation phase of the laboratory course, resuscitative and other safety equipment and procedures, including those shown in Fig. 2-1, are introduced and demonstrated. General rules and regulations regarding the use of the exercise physiology laboratory are reviewed, and a checkout of each student's ability to work safely and effectively is made by the instructor.

Rules of the laboratory

1. The laboratory is used only for obtaining data for approved studies. It is not to be used for recreational exercise, therapy, or training unless the exercise sessions are a part of an approved study wherein data are obtained.

2. Only medically certified subjects may perform exercise.

3. All exercise test protocols that may require maximum or near-maximum effort require medical approval.

4. All subjects who are scheduled to perform maximum or near-maximum effort exercise tests must be medically reviewed immediately before being tested.

5. The exposure of any subject to exercise, including a 15-minute recovery period, must be supervised by two or more authorized observers who are trained in resuscitation procedures.

6. The subject's file must be in the hands of the operator during every exercise

exposure so that proper work loadings may be applied and so that current data entries may be made on appropriate forms in the file.

7. Only authorized observers may operate any item of laboratory equipment, including exercise devices. No subject may make settings or adjustments or may commence exercise without signal by an observer.

EMERGENCY MEASURES
Heart-Lung Resuscitation

IF UNCONSCIOUS

Airway - **Open by tilting head back**

IF NOT BREATHING

Breathe - **Inflate lungs rapidly 3-5 times**

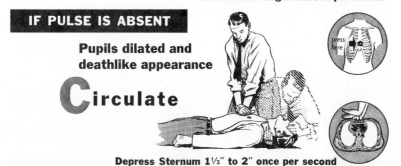

mouth-to-mouth
mouth-to-nose

mouth-to-airway adjunct or bag and mask

IF CAROTID PULSE IS PRESENT
continue 12 lung inflations per minute

IF PULSE IS ABSENT

Pupils dilated and deathlike appearance

Circulate

press here

Depress Sternum 1½" to 2" once per second

CONTINUE RESUSCITATION until spontaneous pulse returns

YOUR
HEART
ASSOCIATION

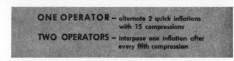

ONE OPERATOR – alternate 2 quick inflations with 15 compressions
TWO OPERATORS – interpose one inflation after every fifth compression

produced by the American Heart Association • 44 East 23rd Street, New York, N.Y. 10010

COPYRIGHT 1965
EM 395 C
1 and 2-65-66-45M
5-67-25M

Fig. 2-1. Mouth-to-mouth resuscitation and external cardiac massage. (Courtesy American Heart Association, Inc., New York.)

FORM 2

Personal data

Name _____ Date _____
　　　　First　　　　Middle　　　　Last

Social Security _____ Sex _____
　　　　　　　　　Number　　　　　　　　　　Male or female

Permanent address _____
　　　　　　　　　Number　　　　Street　　　　Apartment number

_____
City　　　　State　　　　Zip code　　　　Country

Telephone _____
　　　　　Area code　　　　Number　　　　Extension

Present address _____
if different　　Number　　　　Street　　　　Apartment number
from above

_____
City　　　　State　　　　Zip code　　　　Country

Telephone _____
　　　　　Area code　　　　Number　　　　Extension

Occupation _____
　　　　　　Job title or student major

Business address _____
　　　　　　　　Name of business or college

_____
Number　　　　Street　　　　Department

_____
City　　　　State　　　　Zip code　　　　Country

Telephone _____
　　　　　Area code　　　　Number　　　　Extension

Name of next of kin _____ Relation _____
　　　　　　　　First　　Middle　　Last

Address _____
　　　　Number　　　　Street　　　　Apartment number

_____
City　　　　State　　　　Zip code　　　　Country

Telephone _____
　　　　　Area code　　　　Number　　　　Extension

FORM 2—cont'd

Date of birth _____ Age _____
           Day   Month   Year   Years   Months

Place of birth _____
              City   State   Country

Marital status _____
                   Single, married, divorced or widowed

Children _____
        Number

Name of personal physician _____
                    First   Middle   Last

   Office address _____
                    Number   Street   Office

             _____
         City   State   Zip code   Country

   Office telephone _____
               Area code   Number   Extension

   Home address _____
              Number   Street   Apartment

             _____
         City   State   Zip code   Country

   Home telephone _____
               Area code   Number   Extension

8. Data obtained during exercise tests are interpreted to the subject only by professional members of the laboratory staff. Nonprofessional staff members are forbidden to give technical information to subjects.

9. Although the laboratory, due to the presence of exercise devices and locker and shower facilities, may have a gymnasium or clublike appearance, no loitering, smoking, eating, or conversation with subjects is permitted. Under no circumstance is encouragement by a bystander given to a subject during an exercise test, because such motivation contaminates the study and may endanger the subject by masking the responses which would normally indicate to the operator that end points of exercise tolerance were being reached. A disparaging remark also aborts the test.

10. All exercise devices, instruments, tools, and other objects in the laboratory are used routinely and therefore must be kept in their places and never loaned or used outside the laboratory.

Students who already possess some of the skills and knowledge of safety procedures assist the instructor in checking the proficiency of other class members.

During this familiarization and safety checkout phase, the student completes a personal data form (Form 2).

Before volunteering as a subject or serving as an operator for exercise tests, each student familiarizes himself with rejection criteria, end points of tolerance to exercise, and responses that require medical review.

Rejection criteria

The following preexercise conditions indicate that the subject is not at the time ready for an exercise test:

1. Evidence of an intercurrent infection, such as infection of the upper respiratory tract
2. Atypical responses at the end of a 5-minute rest period in the reclining position, such as:
   a. Heart rate 100 beats per minute or above
   b. Respiratory rate 40 per minute or above
   c. Systolic blood pressure 170 mm. Hg or above
   d. Diastolic blood pressure 100 mm. Hg or above
   e. Abnormal electrocardiogram
   f. Oral temperature below 98° F., or above 99.5° F.
3. Atypical responses while standing after the period of reclining rest, such as:
   a. Heart rate less than reclining, or more than 20 beats per minute above reclining
   b. Diastolic blood pressure less than reclining, or more than 30 mm. Hg above reclining
   c. Change in the electrocardiogram
   d. Tendency toward fainting or dizziness

End points of tolerance to exercise

As a precautionary operational procedure during the course of prolonged or intensive exercise, the appearance of the following events are predetermined to be causes for terminating the exercise:

1. Volitional (invisible) end points
   a. Signal from the subject that he is unwilling to continue ("panic button" or "chicken switch")
   b. Complaint of discomfort, fatigue, tiredness, or illness
   c. Distress, irritation, or anxiety
   d. Palpitations, chest pressure, or pains of anginal pattern referred to shoulder, arm, jaw, teeth, or ear
   e. Insistent stitch in side or breathlessness
   f. Lightheadedness, dizziness, drowsiness, syncope, faintness, nausea, headache, malaise, lethargy, weakness, or "unwell" feeling
   g. Claudication (discomfort or pain in legs)
   h. Pounding or throbbing of pulse felt in the head
   i. Muscle weakness, cramping, twitching, spasm, ache, or pain
   j. Cold sweating
2. Subjective (visible but unmeasurable) end points
   a. Ataxic gait, uncoordinated movements, trembling, shakiness, tremor, awkwardness, unsteadiness, wavering or faltering, inability to keep rhythm

   b. Dyspnea (shortness of breath) or hyperpnea (disproportionate hyperventilation, labored or rapid breathing)

   c. Cyanosis (blueing of lips or nail beds)

   d. Change in color of face to ashen or pale

   e. Vomiting

   f. Weakness of voice, postural slumping, or reduction of vigor

   g. Mental confusion, disorientation, inattention, lethargy, stupor, visual disturbances

   h. Expression of distress or anxiety

   i. Diminished pulse

   j. Clammy skin

3. Objective (measurable) end points

   a. Submaximal target end points, age-adjusted

| | | Ages | |
Physiological	Under 35	35-55	Over 55
Heart rate	200	180	160
Systolic blood pressure	240	220	200
Diastolic blood pressure	130	120	110
Respiration rate	55	50	45
Body temperature (°C.)	37.9	38.3	37.8
Energy expenditure (kcal./min.)	16	12	8
Energy expenditure (MET)	15	11	7
Ergometric			
Work rate (watts)	400	300	200
Work rate (kg.-m./min.)	2400	1800	1200

   b. Physiological indices of exercise limits

     (1) Oxygen uptake plateaus while heart rate is increasing (maximum oxygen uptake)

     (2) Respiratory quotient (R.Q.) rises above unity (1.0)

     (3) Ventilation increases abnormally, as expressed by the respiratory equivalent for oxygen:

$$ERO_2 = \frac{\text{Ventilation (L./min.)}}{O_2 \text{ consumption (L./min.)}}$$

     (4) Sharp rise in oxygen pulse (heart rate/O_2)

     (5) Sharp rise in time-tension index (heart rate × systolic blood pressure)

     (6) Systolic blood pressure becomes stabilized or does not rise in proportion to exercise loading

     (7) Pulse pressure decreases

   c. Electrocardiographic indices of exercise limits (Chapter 7)

     (1) Ischemic S-T segment depression; horizontal or descending character, of more than 1 mm. (0.2 mV.)

     (2) Unusual degree of S-T junction depression

     (3) S-T elevation

     (4) Inconsistent S-T junction length

     (5) Ischemic T wave changes

(6) Nonspecific T wave changes

(7) Appearance of U waves

(8) Sudden decrease in the pulse rate

(9) Prolongation of the Q-T interval

(10) Extrasystoles, other than occasional

(11) Paroxysmal supraventricular and ventricular arrhythmias (three or more consecutive ventricular premature beats) and ventricular extrasystoles supervening before the end of T wave (Isolated extrasystoles are no reason for stopping unless they are aggravated or precipitated by exercise.)

(12) A-V block

(13) Ventricular bigemini

(14) Nodal rhythm

(15) Ventricular tachycardia or fibrillation

(16) Paroxysmal atrial tachycardia, flutter or fibrillation

(17) Any failure of the electrocardiograph monitoring system

Responses requiring medical review

The following exercise and postexercise response indicate a medical review before further participation in vigorous exercise:

1. Any of the responses listed above that are severe or persist following exercise
2. Diastolic blood pressure remaining 30 mm. Hg or more over the resting level at 3 minutes after exercise
3. Ischemic S-T segment depression, arrhythmias, or other electrocardiographic end points occurring at any time after exercise
4. Failure of the heart rate to slow by 20 beats within 3 minutes following exercise with terminal heart rate of 120 beats per minute or higher
5. Irregular heart rate following exercise
6. Postexercise syncope, lightheadedness, dizziness, nausea, vomiting, headache, or feeling of malaise
7. Persistent fatigue
8. Substernal discomfort, shortness of breath, retrosternal burning, vague and nondescript chest pains, or indigestion and influenza-like symptoms following exercise
9. Aggravation of musculoskeletal problems
10. Unusual weight loss

Material in the three lists included here constitutes the basis for decision making while monitoring a human subject during an exercise test. Such guides do not relieve the investigator of the responsibility for prudence in the control of human subjects during experimentation, but these criteria, especially the objective type, improve the yield of data that can be analyzed. The criteria also lessen the demands on the subject and the operator to try to make rational assessments of exercise responses and capabilities.

During the course of prolonged or extremely stressful exercise it occasionally happens that personality alterations occur that tend to make the subject tired, hostile, or antagonistic. These lead to falsification of subjective assessment. However, a volitional end point is always available to a subject. The use of a "panic button" or "chicken switch" device constitutes an end point that is subjective, but it is a measure of motivation in that it indicates the subject's unwillingness to continue exposing himself to stress.

The work rate at which predetermined end points occur is used to demonstrate the exercise level that each individual can achieve without limiting reactions. This is the person's physical working capacity (PWC), and it can be employed to evaluate work habits (Chapter 15) and to assess the progress of training or disease.

In the final analysis, the end point of any experiment is defined by the ability of the subject to perform his assigned task in a satisfactory manner. When performance decrement occurs before a physiological end point is reached, it eliminates the need for any decision as to whether or not to continue in the face of a deteriorating state.

Until a subject's exercise response has been observed repeatedly, loads are applied in moderately graded steps and the reactions for a sufficiently long period at each plateau are evaluated before deciding to advance to more intensive levels. Only in proven subjects is it safe to apply abrupt and intensive loads.

Monitoring of exercise response by using the electrocardiogram, blood pressure measurement, and other methods of clinical diagnosis invites the danger of drawing the subject's attention to his health and physical fitness and fostering hypochondriasis. An offhand remark by the examiner about a peculiar pattern in the electrocardiogram or the seemingly high blood pressure may be misinterpreted by the examinee. Thus examiners never make such comments.

Early termination of a test because some end point has been reached is another possible cause of alarm to the examinee. He wants to know why the examiner felt it dangerous for him to continue the exercise test; the answer given by the examiner must assure him that the action was a precautionary operational procedure and in no way indicates that there is anything wrong.

If unusual responses are observed, the examiner terminates the exercise by saying "That's enough for today." After the examinee has left the laboratory the examiner submits the record to a medical consultant who determines if a recall of the subject for review is warranted.

HUMAN SUBJECTS IN THE EXERCISE LABORATORY
Policy and procedure

All projects involving studies of human subjects must meet certain requirements such as those recommended by the Declaration of Geneva of the World Medical Association, the International Code of Medical Ethics, the Declaration of Helsinki, and the Nuremberg Code of Ethics in Medical Research. These requirements grow from a moral, ethical, and legal concern for the welfare of an individual who may be subjected to painful, dangerous, and embarrassing or humilitating experiences in the course of his participation in laboratory studies. It is assumed that he has a basic right to be secure in his person, to receive proper professional care, to enjoy privacy and confidentiality in the use of information about himself, and to be free from undue embarrassment, discomfort, and harassment.

The legal view of experimental procedures utilizing human subjects is that no one has the right to experiment with such individuals, regardless of their signed consent and waiver of responsibility. There is no escape should some untoward reaction take place. The best defense against charge of negligence is an adherence to accepted professional procedures. In exercise physiology these are as follows:

1. Subject is a volunteer.
2. Subject understands the nature of the hazard involved.
3. Probable gain in knowledge is commensurate with the potential risks to the subject.

FORM 3

Subject's consent

Subject's name: _____ Date: _____

I hereby authorize _____
Name of person(s) who will perform procedure(s)
or investigation(s)

and/or such assistants as may be selected by him to perform the following procedure(s)
and investigation(s) (describe in detail):

on _____ .
Subject

The procedure(s) and investigation(s) listed in paragraph 1 has (have) been explained to
me by _____ .
(Name)

I understand that the procedure(s) and investigation(s) described in paragraph 1 involve
the following possible risks and discomforts (describe in detail):

and that the potential benefits of the investigation are as follows:

I understand that I may terminate my participation in the study at any time.

Subject's signature: _____

Witness: _____

4. After considering all possible precautions, safety measures, and preliminary experimentation, the investigator is satisfied the risk is acceptable.
5. Rights and welfare of the subject are protected.
6. Informed consent of the subject is secured (Form 3).

Prior animal experimentation does not guarantee that the same stress will be acceptable by human subjects. Human behavior or response cannot be predicted from data based on animal experimentation.

In the experimental procedures described in this manual special precautions are taken to assure protection of the dignity of the subjects. Only socially acceptable techniques are employed, and subjects receive every consideration for their comfort and well-being.

When familiarity with these observations governing the control of exercise is assured, the experimental phase of the course commences as described above.

INDEPENDENT ORIGINAL RESEARCH

Usually by midterm every student has (1) mastered several laboratory techniques, (2) achieved competence in investigative procedures, and (3) discovered a problem that he has a personal interest in solving.

He may then (1) enlist his team in performing his study at the appropriate experiment station; (2) obtain the approval of the instructor to collaborate with fellow students in performing the investigation outside of class; (3) assist a professor who is carrying out some line of investigation; (4) document his own physiological responses to exercise under unusual exposures, such as mountain-climbing expedition; (5) measure the changes in physiological responses to exercise due to ordinary incidents occurring during the course, such as alterations in exercise habits, illnesses, seasonal variations in climate, day-night cycle, travel, sleeplessness, and other forms of stress; (6) elucidate a physiological mechanism possibly related to a phenomenon of exercise—such as strength, endurance, or speed of movement—by literature search and laboratory study.

Original investigations of the physiological phenomena of exercise usually require the construction or modification of one or more special instruments for the project. This is often accomplished without the aid of a technician or craftsman.

The student may supplement the facilities of the exercise physiology laboratory for his independent research by arrangements to use laboratories of other organizations such as departments of physiology, chemistry, physics, zoology, psychology, engineering, and medicine.

Proficiency check

Task	Date completed	Instructor's initials
1. Formulate preliminary ideas for independent original research projects (Form 1).		
2. Be familiar with roles investigators play in laboratory experimentation.		
3. Know local rules and regulations regarding laboratory use.		
4. Understand requirements to be met by a subject in exercise experiments.		
5. Complete personal data record (Form 2).		

(Continued.)

Task	Date completed	Instructor's initials
6. Be familiar with responses to exercise.	_____	_____
7. Be informed on policy regarding human subjects.	_____	_____
8. Know resuscitation techniques.	_____	_____

SUGGESTED READING

Anthony, C. P.: Anatomy and physiology laboratory manual, ed. 8, St. Louis, 1971, The C. V. Mosby Co.

Bruce, R., Hornsten, T., and Blackmon, J.: Myocardial infarction after normal responses to maximal exercise, Circulation **38**:552, 1968.

Cooper, K.: Guidelines in the management of the exercising patient, J.A.M.A. **211**:1663, 1970.

Hornsten, T., and Bruce, R.: Stress testing, safety precautions, and cardiovascular health, J. Occup. Med. **10**:640, 1968.

Jude, J., and Elan, J.: Fundamentals of cardiopulmonary resuscitation, Philadelphia, 1965, F. A. Davis Co.

Morehouse, L., and O'Connell, E.: A plan for gradually equipping a physical education research laboratory, J. Health, Phys. Educ. Rec. **29**:28, 1958.

Style manual for biological journals, ed. 2, 1966. Available at American Institute of Biological Sciences, 3900 Wisconsin Ave. N.W., Washington, D. C. 20016.

Tuttle, W. W., Schottelius, B. A., and Thomson, J. D.: Physiology laboratory manual, ed. 2, St. Louis, 1968, The C. V. Mosby Co.

van der Smissen, M. E.: Legal liability of cities and schools for injuries in recreation and parks, Cincinnati, 1968, The W. H. Anderson Co.

CHAPTER 3

MUSCULAR PERFORMANCE

THEORY

Morehouse, L. E., and Miller, A. T., Jr.: Physiology of exercise, ed. 6, St. Louis, 1971, The C. V. Mosby Co., chaps. 1, 2, 3, 7.

Åstrand, P-O., and Rodahl, K.: Textbook of work physiology, New York, 1970, McGraw-Hill Book Co., chap. 4.

Muscular performance is analyzed in terms of its physical parameters: force, work, power, and endurance. When the term "strength" is used, it usually refers to the tension that contracting muscles can develop; but actually it is the external physical dynamics that are evaluated. (See Table 1.) It is probably not possible voluntarily to engage a muscle maximally, since there seems to be a reserve that appears during emergencies. Thus in the laboratory total muscular strength or endurance cannot be measured.

Table 1. Muscular strength measurement techniques

Type of contraction	Technique of measuring strength
Isometric (static) pulling	Contraction against an outer resistance that is immovable (i.e., the resistance is too much for the muscle groups to overcome). Muscles develop tension, but length remains constant and no perceptible joint movement is allowed. The outer resistance indicated on a dynamometer is in direct ratio to the muscular force applied.
Isometric (static) breaking	Contraction against an outer resistance that is acting to overcome the tension developed by the muscle. Muscle length remains constant and no joint movement is allowed. The outer resistance is progressively increased until the force of muscle contraction is overcome. The resistance indicated on a dynamometer measures the muscular force applied.
Isotonic (dynamic) concentric (shortening)	Contraction against an outer resistance that can be overcome and moved (e.g., against the force of gravity acting on a load). Muscle shortens during contraction and does work equal to the product of the resistance overcome and the distance of movement.
Isotonic (dynamic) eccentric (lengthening)	Contraction against an outer resistance that tends to lengthen the muscle (e.g., by moving the skeletal segments to which the muscle is attached). The outer resistance is in direct ratio to the force applied by the muscle.
Isokinetic	Contraction, either concentric or eccentric, against an outer resistance that can be moved. The speed of movement is held constant. The outer resistance is in direct ratio to the force applied by the muscle through the course of movement.

TERMINOLOGY

force That which tends to or in actuality does produce or prevent motion. Effect produced by overcoming an object or resisting it. The unit of force is the meter-kilogram, the inch-pound, or a derived unit such as the newton or the dyne.

load Physical agent that is the source of resistance. The act of applying resistance.

resistance Force that, when acting in opposition to a contracting muscle, will cause tension to develop in the muscle.

torque Force perpendicular to a lever arm that is rotating about an axis of rotation. The torque force developed by muscles in any joint position is equal to the load acting perpendicularly to the limb (force) and the length of the limb (moment arm).

FORMULAS
Work

Action of a force over a specific distance in space, or the product of muscular force exerted through specific ranges of movement, is termed work:

$$W = Fs \tag{1}$$

where W (work) = F (force) × s (distance mass is moved)

Units are kilogram-meters.

Power

Power is the rate of doing work, or the work output of muscles at specific speeds of contraction:

$$P = \frac{W}{T} \tag{2}$$

$$\text{where P (power)} = \frac{W \text{ (work)}}{T \text{ (time)}}$$

Units are joules (newtons per meter), seconds, and watts (joules per second).

Total strength index (S_T)

An index of total body strength is obtained by dividing the sum of the strengths of certain body areas by the total body weight:

$$S_T = \frac{LG + RG + LS + BS}{W} \tag{3}$$

where LG = left grip strength
RG = right grip strength
LS = leg lift strength
BS = back lift strength
W = body weight

Units are kilograms.

DYNAMOMETRY

The strength of one muscle group cannot serve as a general indicator of a person's muscle strength because strength depends upon the amount of use that particular muscle group gets during daily activities. Therefore, it is necessary to measure the strength of several groups to attain a general picture of the muscular performance capacity.

Isometric measurement of muscular strength (Table 1) is preferred to other types of contraction because of the variability of results due to the speed of move-

---

FORM 4

Dynamometer calibration

Dynamometer _____   Date _____
       Serial number

Calibrator _____
             Name   Organization

Setting	Trial	True value		Instrument reading	
		kg.	lb.	kg.	lb.
	1				
	2				
	3				
	1				
	2				
	3				
	1				
	2				
	3				

---

ment under dynamic conditions. Further, the dynamometric equipment necessary for isometric measurement can be made quite simple and versatile.

Dynamometer calibration

Calibrate dynamometers by suspending known weights, being sure that the direction of force is in line with the action of the apparatus. Always include the weight of attachment devices. Stamp a serial number on each dynamometer for identification. Store the calibration records (Form 4) in the laboratory files. Recalibrate dynamometers before each testing program begins.

Grip strength measurement
Materials

☐ Adjustable grip dynamometer
☐ Block of magnesium chalk or magnesium carbonate powder

Procedure

☐ Adjust the handle of the dynamometer to fit the hand.
☐ Set the needle indicator at zero.
☐ The subject, standing with hand chalked, takes the dynamometer comfortably in the hand, holding it in line with the forearm, and letting it hang down by the thigh. The second joint of each finger fits snugly under the handle and takes the weight of the instrument, which is then gripped between the fingers and the palm at the base of the thumb (Fig. 3-1).

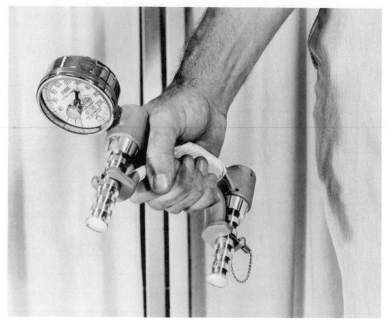

Fig. 3-1. Handgrip strength. See text for procedure. (Courtesy NASA.)

☐ When firmly held, the dynamometer is raised clear of the body, and the wrist is flexed and extended to exert a preliminary stretch of the gripping muscles.

☐ Hand is dorsiflexed, forming a 35-degree angle with the forearm.

☐ The dynamometer is then squeezed vigorously, the subject exerting the maximum force of which he is capable.

☐ During the test neither the hand nor the dynamometer must be permitted to contact the body or any other object. The arm is maintained in an extended position and not swung or pumped violently to add accelerative force.

☐ A shout of encouragement by the experimenter immediately before the effort and a shout by the subject during the peak of the effort will yield scores nearer to the true maximum strength.

☐ Obtain two readings, informing the subject of his score after each reading.

☐ Allow a 30-second rest between attempts. Note each score and count the better result.

Other strength measurements

Various devices using mechanical and electrical dynamometers, cable tensiometers, and constant-speed lever systems have been developed to measure static and dynamic strength and endurance of different muscle groups. In one electrical method a load cell is used to translate changes of force into changes in voltage. The change in output voltage is then amplified and recorded graphically.

Apparatus and procedures for measuring leg lift strength and back lift strength are shown in Fig. 3-2. A technique of measuring isokinetic flexion and extension strength and endurance is shown in Fig. 3-3. Other methods are described in the literature listed under Suggested Reading at the end of this chapter.

There are numerous ways muscle performance can be studied other than the test procedures cited above. A few of the different types of application of muscular

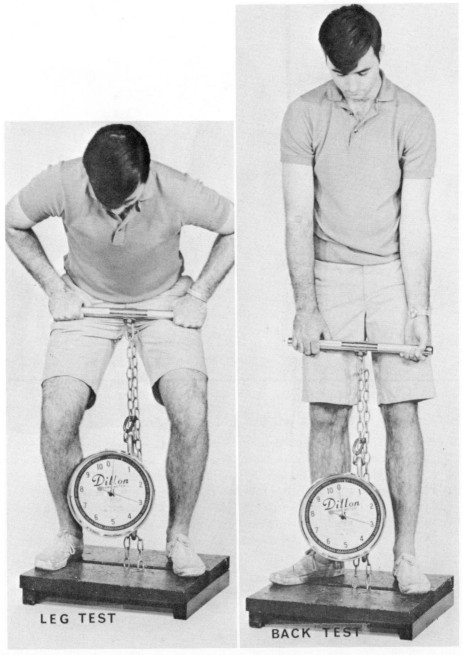

Fig. 3-2. Leg lift strength (left) measured with knees bent to angle of 130 to 140 degrees. With handlebar across thighs, and without using the back, knees are slowly but vigorously extended. Back lift strength (right) is measured with legs straight and handlebar at arm's length. Without leaning backward, pull upward using the back muscles. Maximum indicator remains at peak load. (Courtesy W. C. Dillon & Co., Inc., Van Nuys, Calif.)

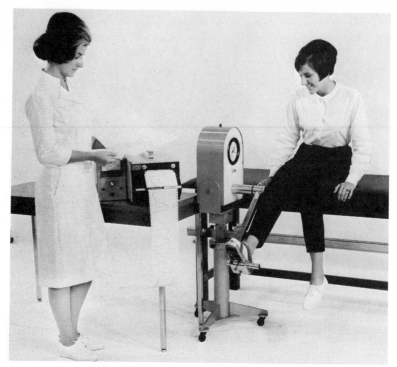

Fig. 3-3. Isokinetic knee flexion and extension. (Courtesy Technicon Cybex, Inc., Tarrytown, N. Y.)

force are shown in Table 2. Each type of contraction can be recorded on a strip chart and its significant characteristics measured for the purpose of studying the physiological mechanisms of muscular strength and endurance.

CHECKLIST FOR REPORTING MUSCLE STRENGTH MEASUREMENTS

Results of strength tests depend on the subject's intrinsic muscular capability, the stabilization of his body, his motivation to exert a certain portion of his strength, the method he uses to contract his muscles, and the recording techniques employed. To interpret and compare the results it is necessary to explain the experimental methods. Since scores recorded by different instruments vary widely, specify the make of dynamometer used. A checklist (Form 5) developed by Kroemer and Howard is an aid for complete reporting. Cross references in the list show the multiple effects of single factors.

MYOTONOMETRY

The hardness of muscle and its adjacent tissues in relaxed and contracted states can be measured using a muscle tone meter. The meter shown in Fig. 3-4 is a cylinder containing a spring with a retractable ball at one end and a gauge at the other end. The ball is placed over the muscle being investigated and is slowly pressed into the tissues until the flange of the cylinder is in full contact with the skin. The extent of retraction of the ball is registered on the gauge.

When muscle tone in the relaxed state is measured, the lowest of three readings is recorded. In the contracted state the highest of three readings is registered.

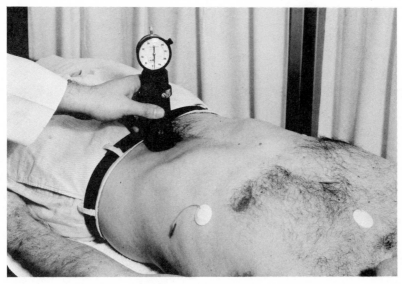

Fig. 3-4. Muscle tone meter. (Courtesy NASA.)

Table 2. Types of application of muscular force

Type of contraction	Strip chart record	Significant characteristics to be measured
Fast single maximal		Peak force Contraction speed Relaxation speed
Slow single maximal		Peak force Force decay (slope)
Sustained single 80% maximal		Endurance (time) Tremor onset (time, amplitude)
Fast repetitive, maximal effort and frequency, 10 seconds		Force Frequency Work output Power
Sustained 10 seconds alternating with rest 10 seconds, 200 seconds		Force Force decay (fatigue) Work output Power
Fast single maximal every second until exhaustion		Force Force decay (fatigue) Exhaustion (time) Work output Power

FORM 5

Kroemer and Howard checklist for reporting muscle strength measurements*

Measuring device
    General identification
- [ ] function
- [ ] model, manufacturer
- [ ] last calibration
- [ ] Attachment of measuring device to the subject
    Output-readout
- [ ] digital/analog
- [ ] units read
- [ ] Other (specify)

Location of the force vector
- [ ] Static force exertion (no motion): coordinates of the point of force application and direction of force
    Dynamic force exertion (motion):
- [ ] coordinates of the path of the force application
- [ ] direction of force along the path
- [ ] motion on the path (temporary location, speed, acceleration)
- [ ] masses accelerated or decelerated
- [ ] Other (specify)

Subject
- [ ] Drawn from what population
- [ ] Anthropometric data
- [ ] Other (specify)

Posture of the subject
- [ ] Coupling of the subject to the measuring device (see Attachment of measuring device to the subject)
- [ ] Body parts and muscles chiefly used
- [ ] Body posture during force exertion
- [ ] Body support/reaction force available
- [ ] Other (specify)

Method of force exertion
Exact wording of the instructions given to the subject; or, especially if no specific instructions given; how force was actually exerted—in particular:
- [ ] Requested magnitude of force (all-out effort, or submaximal)
    Requested manner of force exertion
- [ ] how to build up force
- [ ] what to do after requested magnitude has been reached
- [ ] how long to exert force
- [ ] is muscle length kept constant during exertion (isometric)
- [ ] is muscle tension kept constant during exertion (isotonic)
- [ ] Time interval between subsequent tests
- [ ] How many repetitions
- [ ] Practice/training
- [ ] Other (specify)

Motivational factors
- [ ] Selection of subjects
- [ ] Voluntary/required participation
- [ ] Mode of payment

*From Kroemer, K., and Howard, J.: Problems in assessing muscle strength, Wright-Patterson Air Force Base, Ohio, 1970, Aerospace Medical Division, Air Force Systems Command.

FORM 5—cont'd

☐ Knowledge of the purpose of the experiment
☐ Knowledge of the experimental procedure
☐ Feedback of performance
☐ Supervision during the experiment
☐ Stimulating factors such as encouragments, rewards, competition, spectators
☐ Restraining factors such as danger, fear of injuries, adverse environmental conditions, fatigue, lack of interest, spectators
☐ Other (specify)

Selection of performance score
☐ Amplitude-dependent value (maximum, minimum, or . . .)
☐ Time-dependent value (at or over a specified time)
☐ Other (specify)

ERGOGRAPHY

Local muscular endurance is assessed by registering the decrement in force exerted by muscle groups, either while holding static positions of strain for prolonged periods of time (local static muscular endurance) or while performing continued repetitive movements for as long as possible (local dynamic muscular endurance). Techniques of measurement are described in Table 3. Dynamic endurance measurement is preferred to the static type because of the difficulty in motivating subjects to continue static effort.

The instrument for registering force decrements is the *ergograph* (ergo = work, graph = registration). Various types of ergographs have been developed for measuring the local muscular fatigue of the finger flexors, and the arm, leg, and foot movements.

When a simple movement involving only a few muscles is to be evaluated, a finger ergograph is used. The palm of the hand and all fingers but one are immobilized; the free finger raises and lowers a load in rhythm with a metronome. Work is computed by multiplying the height of each lift by the weight of the load

Table 3. Muscular endurance measurement

Type of contraction	Technique of measuring contraction endurance
Static endurance	Interval of time that muscle groups can exert a specific force by contracting against an immovable outer resistance; or, the ability of muscle groups to exert force by holding a static contraction against an immovable outer resistance over a specified prolonged interval of time
Dynamic endurance	Interval of time that muscle groups can perform continued repetitive movements at a specific speed of contraction against a specific resistance through a specific range of movement; or, the capacity of muscle groups to extend the power output at a specific speed of contraction through a specific range of movement over a specific prolonged interval of time

SAMPLE DATA SHEET

Total strength index $(S_T) = \dfrac{LG + RG + LS + BS}{W}$ (Formula 3)

Name	LG (kg.)	RG (kg.)	LS (kg.)	BS (kg.)	Sum of first 4 columns (kg.)	W (kg.)	$S_T = $ sum/W
Example	54.0	55.8	242.2	180.1	532.1	75	7.09

and then adding them up. Forearm and leg ergographs are designed and used in the same manner.

When gross muscular effort is desired in order to tax the cardiovascular, respiratory, and metabolic systems, an ergometer as described in Chapter 14 is used.

Proficiency check

Task	Date completed	Instructor's initials
1. Know correct terminology.	_____	_____
2. Be familiar with types of strength (Tables 1 to 3).	_____	_____
3. Calibrate a dynamometer (Form 4).	_____	_____

Task	Date completed	Instructor's initials
4. Demonstrate strength test techniques.	_____	_____
5. Demonstrate myotonometry techniques.	_____	_____
6. Demonstrate ergographic techniques (Table 2).	_____	_____

Sample experiments

☐ Correlate muscle strength with factors such as muscle tone, sex, age, body size, and state of training.

☐ Examine the effects of load, rate, and duration of effort and rest periods on local muscular fatigue and muscle tone.

☐ Combine electromyographic (Chapter 4) and plethysmographic techniques to study neuromuscular and circulatory factors in muscular endurance.

☐ Note the constancy of the strength of a muscle group expressed in terms of the transsectional area (kilograms of force per square centimeter of muscle area) among men and women of different ages and states of training.

☐ Select subjects of different heights who are geometrically similar and examine the relationship of muscle strength.

☐ Note how the state of training affects muscle size, strength, and tone.

☐ Plan an original independent research investigation to elucidate the phenomena of muscle strength or tone, or to derive an understanding of the mechanism of strength development.

REFERENCE

Kroemer, K., and Howard, J.: Problems in assessing muscle strength, Wright-Patterson Air Force Base, Ohio, 1970, Aerospace Medical Division, Air Force Systems Command.

SUGGESTED READING

Asmussen, E.: Exercise—general statement of unsolved problems, Circ. Res. 20:1, 1967.

Berger, R. A.: Comparison of the effect of various weight training loads on strength, Res. Quart. Amer. Ass. Health Phys. Educ. 36:141, 1965.

Chui, E.: Effects of isometric and dynamic weight-training exercises upon strength and speed of movement, Res. Quart. Amer. Ass. Health Phys. Educ. 35:246, 1964.

Clarke, D.: Effect of immersion in hot and cold water upon recovery of muscular strength following fatiguing isometric exercise, Arch. Phys. Med. 44:565, 1963.

Clarke, D., and Stull, G.: Endurance training as a determinant of strength and fatigability, Res. Quart. Amer. Ass. Health Phys. Educ. 41:19, 1970.

Clarke, H.: Muscular strength and endurance in man, Englewood Cliffs, N. J., 1966, Prentice-Hall, Inc.

Clarke, H., and Clarke, D.: Developmental and adapted physical education, Englewood Cliffs, N. J., 1963, Prentice-Hall, Inc.

Petty, P. G.: A recording ergometer, Lancet 1: 976, 1963.

Sedgwick, A., and Whalen, H.: Effect of passive warm-up on muscular strength and endurance, Res. Quart. Amer. Ass. Health Phys. Educ. 35:45, 1964.

Singh, M., and Karpovich, P.: Isotonic and isometric forearm flexors and extensors, J. Appl. Physiol. 21:1435, 1966.

Singh, M., and Karpovich, P.: Strength of forearm flexors and extensors in men and women, J. Appl. Physiol. 25:177, 1968.

Start, K., and Graham, J.: Relationship between the relative and absolute isometric endurance of an isolated muscle group, Res. Quart. Amer. Ass. Health Phys. Educ. 35:193, 1964.

Start, K., and Holmes, R.: Local muscular endurance with open and occluded intramuscular circulation, J. Appl. Physiol. 18: 804, 1963.

Thistle, H. G., et al.: Isokinetic contraction—a new concept of resistive exercise, Arch. Phys. Med. 48:279, 1967.

CHAPTER 4

ELECTROMYOGRAPHY (EMG)

THEORY

Morehouse, L. E., and Miller, A. T., Jr.: Physiology of exercise, ed. 6, St. Louis, 1971, The C. V. Mosby Co., chaps. 1, 2, 3.

Åstrand, P-O., and Rodahl, K.: Textbook of work physiology, New York, 1970, McGraw-Hill Book Co., chaps. 4, 16.

Muscle activity can be studied by recording the action potentials, using needle electrodes thrust into the muscle, sewing fine wires into the muscle, or using skin electrodes placed over the contracting muscle. The action potentials (electrical activity) of the motor units are amplified, recorded on a strip chart, observed on an oscilloscope, and listened to on a loudspeaker. The needle or wire electrodes give discrete action potentials which can be analyzed. The surface electrodes (metal plates on the skin) pick up potentials from many different motor units simultaneously, and an integration of these potentials reveals the sum of the motor unit activity.

Studies of the physiology of movement can be made by combining EMG observations with myotonometry (discussed in the previous chapter), electrogoniometry (Chapter 5), ataxiometry (Chapter 6), and electrocardiography (Chapter 7). EMG data can be telemetered for studies of man or animal working remotely.

Since surface EMG, sometimes called skin or percutaneous EMG, does not require sterile procedures and is the most practical for studies of intact man in action, it will be described in detail in this manual. Students interested in needle EMG will find the techniques in the literature cited at the end of this chapter.

TERMINOLOGY

amplifier Circuit that raises or "boosts" the amplitude of the input signal from the electrode or transducer to furnish enough power to operate a recorder or other device. May be split into a *preamplifier* and a *power amplifier*.

coupler Device that provides the accommodation required to interconnect a recorder with a physical system. May also contain circuits that compute time integrals of signals or deliver internal calibration signals.

electrode Device that picks up an electrical signal from one system and conducts this same electrical signal to another system. No conversion takes place.

gain Ratio of the output signal amplitude to the input signal amplitude. Sometimes called *amplification*. The multiplication factor of a device.

noise Unwanted signals. *Inherent noise* arises within the measurement circuit; *interference noise* is picked up from outside the circuit (AC power lines, arcing switches, and broadcast stations). If interference noise is greater than inherent noise, it has to be reduced before inherent noise becomes apparent.

sensitivity Numerical ratio that expresses the voltage amplitude required to cause a pen or meter indicator to deflect a certain amount. The sensitivity may be changed by changing the gain.

transducer Device that is actuated by energy from one system and retransmits energy in a different form to another system. A converter.

MATERIALS

- ☐ Fat-solvent alcohol, 70%, or reagent grade acetone, glass-bottled
- ☐ Cotton swabs, large
- ☐ Emery cloth, 150 grit, or dental burr for dermabrasion
- ☐ Surface electrodes
- ☐ Saline electrode paste
- ☐ Aeroplast and adhesive tape
- ☐ EMG amplifier
- ☐ Volt-ohm resistance meter of low current density
- ☐ Oscilloscope, tape or optical galvanometer recorder
- ☐ Strip chart recorder, multi-channel, with millivolt calibrator, signal marker (pen deflection), and a recording speed of 25 mm. per second
- ☐ High-gain amplifier and audio system

PROCEDURES
Primary (basic, direct) EMG

The primary signal ranges and characteristics of the electromyogram bioelectric potential are as follows: Frequency range is 10 to 2000 Hz,* and pulse duration is 0.6 to 20 msec.

Integrated EMG

Using an integrator coupler or resistor-capacitor, EMG signals can be rectified and then averaged to produce an "integrated" EMG. This record, shown in Fig. 4-1, although not a true time integral because of its limited memory time, is an easily evaluated index of muscle activity. The summed, integrated EMG record permits a meaningful interpretation of relative muscle motion, degree of muscle contraction, and amplitude of muscle action. The averaged integration of the EMG also makes the evaluation of time sequence in muscular activity more convenient. Calibration of the integrated EMG is accomplished by introducing an external square wave.

Precautions

Any AC-powered instrument, such as the EMG power amplifier and recorder, if improperly installed, is a potential shock hazard. To eliminate this hazard:

- ☐ Never use a power line extension cord except one of heavy duty type and of ample current-carrying capacity.
- ☐ Be sure that the power line grounding lead of the instrument case is wired directly to a verified earth ground.
- ☐ Do not use a power cord adapter as an earth ground.
- ☐ Be sure that the chassis of every other AC-powered device, including lamps and radios, in the laboratory is connected to the same verified earth ground through a low-resistance path of less than 1 ohm.
- ☐ Never allow any subject connected to the EMG instruments to be placed in contact with any devices or objects such as metal beds, lamps, water pipes, electrodes, and x-ray machines that are also connected to earth ground.
- ☐ A qualified electrician should carefully check and certify the condition of all AC-powered devices and all grounding wiring in the room.

---

*One hertz (Hz) is one cycle per second. Frequency components up to 150 Hz can be recorded on a strip chart recorder; signals above that level require oscilloscope, tape or optical galvanometer readout.

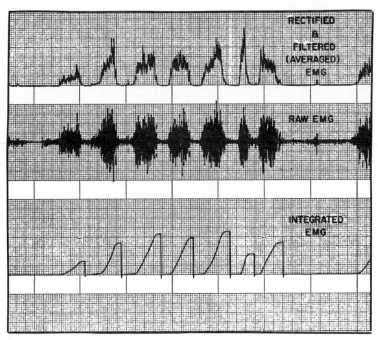

Fig. 4-1. Typical EMG recording traces. (Courtesy Beckman Instruments, Inc., Fullerton, Calif.)

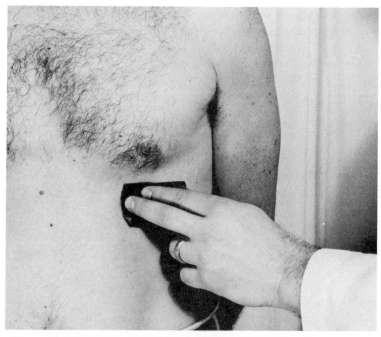

Fig. 4-2. Preparation of skin surface for electrode. Swab the skin three times with copious amounts of 70% alcohol or acetone on cotton, protecting the subject by placing a towel below the site. Allow the skin to dry. Remove the dead scaly cells of the upper layers of the stratum corneum by making six light passes over the site with emery cloth as shown. Avoid thermal irritation and do not draw blood. This preparation provides both low skin resistance and low skin potential. (Courtesy NASA.)

Surface electrode

Lightweight nonpolarizing liquid-junction pure silver–silver chloride disk, 1 cm. in diameter, is encased in a lightweight plastic holder so that a 2 mm. constant distance is maintained between the skin and the contact surface of the electrode. Electrical conduction is accomplished solely by the electrode paste to eliminate excessive baseline drift. The electrode position on the skin is firmly maintained by use of an adhesive disk. The electrode lead wire is a thin flexible cable.

Preparation of electrode site

☐ Shave hair from areas large enough to permit adhesion of tape used to hold electrodes in place.

☐ Cleanse skin with fat-solvent alcohol or acetone.

☐ Anesthetize skin with Xylocaine.

☐ *Dermabrasion, dental burr method.* Remove a very thin superficial horny layer of epidermis with a high-speed drill fitted with a clean, small, oval dental burr applied momentarily to the electrode site. The tiny concavity, about 2 mm. in diameter, thus produced requires a week or so to heal. The operation is painless and no blood is drawn. When the horny layer of skin is removed, the electrode paste goes into solution with the tissue fluids and a liquid junction is established.

☐ *Dermabrasion, emery cloth method.* See Fig. 4-2.

Applying the electrode

☐ Moisten the face of the electrode with a drop of electrode paste, thoroughly saturating the electrode disk. Avoid spreading excess liquid under the plastic holder, as it results in poor adhesion of the electrodes.

☐ Tape electrodes in position with adhesive disks and strips of tape.

☐ Direct the lead wires of the electrodes toward a common area (e.g., over the shoulder) for attachment to the patient cable with a piece of tape placed over the wires at this point to prevent strain on the electrodes.

☐ Attach the electrodes to the patient cable.

Electrode resistance

The small size of the liquid-junction electrode has the disadvantage that because of decreased total skin capacity and increased electrode resistance, even with the recommended high input impedance of the EMGs (100,000 ohms), there may be distortion of the EMG because of the skin capacity and electrode polarization. With a 1 cm. diameter electrode the input impedance must be greater than 200,000 ohms to avoid distortion or loss of signal amplitude. These effects of low impedance can be avoided if separate buffer amplifiers are used at each electrode.

Resistance across the electrodes should be less than 3000 ohms. Resistance is recorded by using a volt-ohm meter and connecting the two terminals to the electrode wires. Use of a multimeter to measure resistance of the skin-electrode system is discouraged because the relatively high current density is extremely detrimental to the silver chloride coating of the electrodes.

Surface EMG procedure

☐ Prepare the skin surface.

☐ Cover electrode with thin film of electrode paste.

☐ Place the search electrode in surface contact with motor units to be studied.

☐ Place the reference electrode over a nearby area where there are few muscles (e.g., wrist or sternum).

☐ Allow minimum interelectrode space of 3 cm.

☐ Place the ground electrode on the ankle on the same side.

☐ Move the search electrode about until the best location for maximal discharge is found.

☐ Seal the electrode disks in place with aeroplast and adhesive paste.

☐ To avoid pull on the electrodes during activity, loop the wires and tape them to the skin a few inches from the electrodes.

☐ Check the electrical resistance of the skin. If it is more than 3000 ohms, remove the electrode and paste and reprepare the skin surface.

☐ Make a test record, designating the magnitude of millivolts on the record, and actuating the signal marker to designate the point of action to be studied.

☐ Commence the experiment.

Reuse of electrodes

Clean the electrodes with alcohol, soap and water, or any standard bactericidal solution. Dip them in sterile normal saline solution and dry them before using.

TELEMETRY

The electromyograms of an exercising subject can be recorded remotely by using radio telemetry. The system consists of a transmitting unit and a receiving unit. The

Fig. 4-3. Telemetry system. EMG input from two surface electrodes over the thigh and ECG input from the two electrodes on the chest of the subject, **A,** are transmitted to the receiver, **B,** where an analog output signal is generated and displayed on an indicating or recording device (not shown). (Woodallen photograph.)

transmitting unit (Fig. 4-3) contains signal conditioners that convert the EMGs or other physiological or environmental data to voltages that modulate an FM transmitter. The EMG and the electrocardiogram (Chapter 7) require an amplifier having a frequency response of 0.1 hertz (Hz) to 100 Hz and a gain of 100. Power is obtained from a battery pack. Data transmitted from up to 300 feet away are detected and amplified by an ordinary FM receiver and sent to a discriminator that generates an analog output signal, which is displayed on indicating or recording devices.

Proficiency check

Task	Date completed	Instructor's initials
1. Calibrate EMG.	_____	_____
2. Prepare electrode site.	_____	_____
3. Apply surface electrode.	_____	_____
4. Measure electrode resistance.	_____	_____
5. Demonstrate EMG measurement.	_____	_____
6. Clean electrodes.	_____	_____

Sample experiments using surface electrodes and integrated EMGs

☐ Demonstrate the activity of a muscle during prescribed movements and postures.
☐ Demonstrate the interplay of coordination of two or more muscles during a prescribed movement.
☐ Use an EMG with a dynamometer and chart the relation of electrical activity to the tension exerted during shortening (concentric) and lengthening (eccentric) contractions.
☐ Study the force-velocity characteristics of various muscles.
☐ Demonstrate voluntary relaxation in a muscle group by reducing EMG activity to near zero.
☐ Study the effect of stretching on EMG activity.
☐ Study the effect of fatigue on EMG activity.
☐ Compare EMG activity during a standard movement of a stiff, sore, or cramped muscle with EMG activity during the same movement when the muscle has recovered.
☐ Study the EMG record during stretching of a cramped muscle.
☐ Study the parts of the deltoid muscle activated in different motions and devise an individual muscle–training program from this analysis.
☐ Present the chronological order of the participation of the major muscles involved in the performance of a task.
☐ Determine how the wearing of high-heeled shoes affects the function of the calf muscles.
☐ Record the EMG of gastrocnemius inhibition as subject tries to rise on tiptoes while standing before the edge of an open door with feet planted on either side and nose and abdomen touching the door edge.
☐ Note the effect of training on the EMG.
☐ Evaluate abdominal muscle exercises by EMG.

SUGGESTED READING

Basmajian, J.: Muscles alive—their functions revealed by electromyography, Baltimore, 1962, The Williams & Wilkins Co.

Broer, M., and Houtz, S.: Patterns of muscular activity in selected sport skills—an electromyographic study, Springfield, Ill., 1967, Charles C Thomas, Publisher.

Day, J.: Review of NASA-MSC electroencephalogram and electrocardiogram electrode systems including application techniques, Washington, D. C., 1968, National Aeronautics and Space Administration.

Galambos, R.: Nerves and muscles, New York, 1962, Anchor Books.

Kay, R.: Experimental biology—measurement and analysis, New York, 1964, Reinhold Publishing Corp.

Malmstadt, H., Enke, C., and Toren, E.: Electronics for scientists, New York, 1962, Benjamin, Inc.

Trank, J., Fetter, J., and Lauer, R.: A spray-on electrode for recording the electrocardiogram during exercise, J. Appl. Physiol. 24:267, 1968.

Tuttle, W. W., Schottelius, B. A., and Thomson, J. D.: Physiology laboratory manual, ed. 2, St. Louis, 1968, The C. V. Mosby Co.

CHAPTER 5

MOBILITY

THEORY

    Morehouse, L. E., and Miller, A. T. Jr.: Physiology of exercise, ed. 6, St. Louis, 1971, The C. V. Mosby Co., chaps. 1, 2, 8, 9.

    Åstrand, P-O., and Rodahl, K.: Textbook of work physiology, New York, 1970, McGraw-Hill Book Co., chap. 12.

The extent to which joints can be moved in controlled maximal motions appears to be a function of (1) the elasticity or stiffness of muscle and connective tissue fibers and (2) the resistive tension produced by the myotatic stretch reflex. Neither the elastic nor the myotatic reflex mechanisms in range-of-motion phenomena have been elucidated. Lacking this basis it is not understood why the freedom to move is limited by diet (vitamin C deficiency), drugs (cortisone), cold, residual neuromuscular tension, adaptive shortening or contracture of muscle and connective tissue, aging, lack of exercise, muscle weakness, pain, injury, and pathological changes (arthritis) leading to partial or complete ankylosis.

Mobility is a specific factor, varying considerably with each joint. There is no single measure of general body mobility.

Range-of-motion comparisons among individuals are affected by anatomical differences such as trunk and arm length.

The term "flexibility" used to describe joint motion capacity implies just flexion and thus is a misnomer. *Mobility* is a more accurate term to describe measures of maximal range of motion of joints.

Several methods employed for the measurement of joint mobility are found in the list of suggested reading at the end of this chapter. Three methods will be described here: sit-and-reach, Flexometer, and goniometer.

SIT-AND-REACH

The sit-and-reach test is conducted with the subject sitting on the floor or bench (Fig. 5-1) with legs extended. Without bending his knees and without using forward momentum, he slowly reaches forward with extended arms and fingers in an attempt to project his fingertips as close to the toes, or as far beyond them, as possible. A ruler is used to measure the distance of the fingertips from the toes. When the bench is used, the subject gradually slides a marker along the shelf in which a ruler is embedded. Instead of the toes, the surface of the footboard is used as the reference point. The best of two attempts is scored.

If the reference point is considered as "zero," and a meter stick is used as a ruler, scores of −30 cm. (fingers not reaching the toes) to +15 cm. (fingers beyond the toes) are typical. See list of representative values on page 36.

FLEXOMETER

Leighton's Flexometer test employs an apparatus consisting of a circular scale (360 degrees) with a weighted dial and a weighted pointer needle, as shown in Fig.

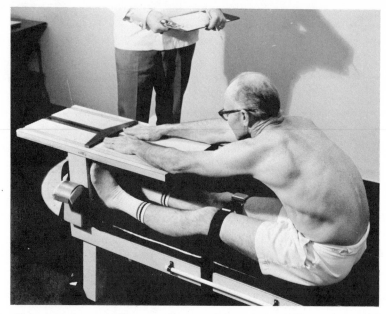

Fig. 5-1. Sit-and-reach test. (Courtesy County of Los Angeles, Department of Personnel, Occupational Health Service.)

Fig. 5-2. Flexometer dial locked in knee flexion position. (Courtesy J. R. Leighton, Cheney, Wash.)

5-2. The instrument is strapped to the body segment being measured, with the dial and pointer set at zero degrees. The mechanics of the instrument are based on the fact that gravity always pulls the weighted end of the needle downward during the execution of a movement. Oscillations of the dial and pointer are damped to reduce measurement time.

In using the instrument the dial is locked at zero degrees at one extreme position (e.g., full flexion of the knee); the movement is made and the pointer locked at the other extreme position (i.e., full extension of the knee). The reading of the pointer on the dial is the arc through which the movement has taken place.

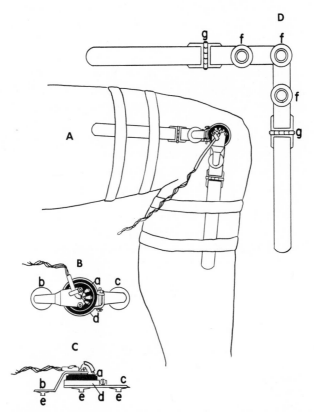

Fig. 5-3. A, Electrogoniometer (elgon) attached to a chassis, which is strapped to the leg. **B,** Top view of the elgon: *a,* potentiometer; *b* and *c,* snap buttons; *d,* a clamp for attaching arms to potentiometer. **C,** Side view of the elgon: *a,* potentiometer; *b* and *c,* arms; *d,* clamp; *e,* studs of snap buttons. **D,** Chassis: *f,* sockets for elgon studs; *g,* hinges. (From Karpovich, P. V., and Sinning, W.: Physiology of muscular activity, Philadelphia, 1971, W. B. Saunders Co.)

Leighton's Flexometer will not work where the measurement must be made in horizontal plane. Also, in some areas there is not room to fasten the Flexometer. Angles are measured without reference to a joint center, but angles of elementary movements can be measured by first identifying reference positions and using zero degrees as a standard when the instrument is attached parallel to the plane in which the angle is to be measured.

Reliable data in comparative studies are obtained by detailed description of measurement techniques so the technique can be repeated. Here is an example of a description by Leighton.

Measure: Knee flexion and extension.
Starting position: Prone position on box or bench with knees at end of and lower legs extending beyond edge of bench, arms at sides of and hands grasping edges of bench. Instrument fastened to outside of either ankle.
Movement: Count (*1*) foot moved upward and backward in an arc to position as near buttocks as possible (Fig. 5-1), dial locked; (*2*) foot moved forward and downward until leg is forcibly extended, pointer locked; (*3*) subject relaxes, reading taken.
Caution: Position of upper leg may not be changed during movement.

GONIOMETER

Joint angles during movement can be measured by using a simple protractor goniometer or Karpovich's electrogoniometer (elgon) as shown in Fig. 5-3. In the electrogoniometer changing positions decrease and increase the resistance within a wire-wound potentiometer and affect the current flow from a constant voltage supplied to the potentiometer. The elgon is calibrated by noting the voltage changes on a strip chart recorder as the angle of the elgon changes each 10 degrees.

The goniometer is used by visually aligning the two arms with appropriate reference lines on the body. The protractor device may contain a bubble level which can be set to any desired reference angle.

Elgon measures of joint motions during complex activities such as swinging a club can be registered by using a terminal electrode box and 10-foot cables to the elgon and the recording equipment. The operator holds the terminal electrode box a few feet from the subject and moves with him. The elgon signal can also be telemetered, using the instruments shown in Fig. 4-3.

Integrated EMG records can be superimposed with the elgon trace to compare patterns of activity.

Representative values

	cm.	in.	degrees
Trunk flexion (sit-and-reach) beyond footboard	+5.0	+2.0	
Trunk extension	38.0	15.0	
Trunk extension-flexion			72.0
Trunk rotation			50.0
Lateral flexion	10.0	4.0	
Hip extension-flexion			104.0

Proficiency check

Task	Date completed	Instructor's initials
1. Demonstrate sit-and-reach test.	_____	_____
2. Demonstrate Flexometer test.	_____	_____
3. Demonstrate goniometer test.	_____	_____

Sample experiments

☐ Conduct 20 sit-and-reach test trials. Note variability and state possible causes.
☐ Correlate range of motion of several joints with age, sex, and athletic experience.
☐ Chart the diurnal variability of joint mobility.
☐ Relate posture or body position to range of motion.
☐ Investigate the effect of warm-up (number of preparatory movements) on maximum range of motion.
☐ Compare the effect of ballistic and static stretching techniques.
☐ Observe the effects of rate and rhythm of stretching procedures on range of motion of various joints.
☐ Measure the differences between range-of-motion measurements, using active and passive movement techniques, and explain the physiological significance of the differences.

☐ Use electromyography (Chapter 4) with joint mobility measures to study the relationship of relaxation to maximum range of motion.

☐ Investigate the effect of stretching exercise on physical performance.

REFERENCES

Adrian, M., Tipton, C. M., and Karpovich, P. V.: Electrogoniometry manual, Springfield, Mass., 1965, Springfield College.

Leighton, J.: The Leighton Flexometer and flexibility test, J. Ass. Phys. Ment. Rehab. **20**:100, 1967.

Leighton, J.: An instrument and technique for the measurement of range of joint motion, Arch. Phys. Med. **36**:571, 1955.

SUGGESTED READING

Doss, W. S., and Karpovich, P. V.: A comparison of concentric, eccentric, and isometric strength of elbow flexors, J. Appl. Physiol. **20**:351, 1965.

Fleishman, E.: The structure and measurement of physical fitness, Englewood Cliffs, N. J., 1964, Prentice-Hall, Inc.

Ricci, B.: Physiological basis of human performance, Philadelphia, 1967, Lea & Febiger.

Tipton, C. M., and Karpovich, P. V.: Clinical electrogoniometry, J. Ass. Phys. Ment. Rehab. **18**:90, 1964.

Zivi, S., and Humberstone, G.: Chest motion visualized by holographic interferometry, Med. Res. Engin., June, 1970.

CHAPTER 6

MOVEMENT DESCRIPTION

THEORY

Morehouse, L. E., and Miller, A. T., Jr.: Physiology of exercise, ed. 6, St. Louis, 1971, The C. V. Mosby Co., chaps. 3, 4, 5, 6, 9.

Åstrand, P-O., and Rodahl, K.: Textbook of work physiology, New York, 1970, McGraw-Hill Book Co., chaps. 4, 16.

In physiological studies of bodily exercise it is necessary to be able to describe and measure postures and movements with clarity, accuracy, and reproducibility. The notation should be in an abbreviated or "shorthand" form that is compatible with common methods of engineering analysis such as drafting layouts, trigonometric analysis, and machine computations. The system should permit either refinement of detailed studies of specific joint motions or extension to complex movement descriptions, such as graphic display by computer as shown in Fig. 6-1.

Concurrent measurements of the exercise event, the environment, the physiological responses, and the behavioral responses are coordinated by using an event recorder that contains several channels. Either a strip chart or an oscillographic camera record of the information is obtained for analysis.

System components such as counters and timers can be operated independently, with one channel assigned to mark the occurrence of the onset and termination of each external measurement.

TERMINOLOGY
Measurement of motion mechanics

scalar Measures magnitude only.
    weight or **mass,** in grams or pounds.
    length, in meters.
    area, or flat surface, in square meters or square inches.
    volume, or space measured by cubic units, in cubic meters or cubic inches.
    time, in seconds.
vector Measures magnitude and direction.
    acceleration, or rate at which the velocity of a moving object changes.
    force, mass × acceleration.
    displacement, or distance from a given point.
    momentum, mass × velocity.
    velocity, speed or instantaneous rate of motion at which displacement occurs in a given direction.

$$\text{Vav} = \text{s/t when:} \quad \begin{aligned} \text{Vav} &= \text{average velocity} \\ \text{s} &= \text{displacement} \\ \text{t} &= \text{elapsed time} \end{aligned}$$

Types of motion

rectilinear Straight line.
rotatory Circular path.
curvilinear Curved path.

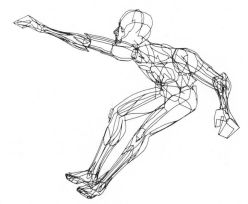

Fig. 6-1. Reach assessment by computer graphic display. The lengths of body links and the paths of motion of the three-dimensional man-model at various positions are graphically displayed in animated film sequences, such as the frame depicted here. The computer models are validated by superimposing them on human movement films. (From Chubb, G. P., et al.: A.M.R.L. TR-70-60, Aerospace Medical Research Laboratory, Wright-Patterson Air Force Base, Ohio.)

Axes of motion

X-axis Longitudinal axis running from front to back of the body. Associated with roll maneuvers, in which the body cartwheels or spins around its **X**-axis.

Y-axis Lateral axis running from side to side of the body. Associated with pitch maneuvers, in which the body turns or somersaults around its **Y**-axis.

Z-axis Vertical axis running from head to foot of the body. Associated with yaw maneuvers, in which the body pivots or twists sideways around its **Z**-axis in lateral movement.

Glossary of timer and chronograph terms

register Small dial on face.

time-out Timepiece can record total time of interrupted operation (side button or side slide).

split Two sweep hands, one hand for timing segments and one hand for timing continuous operation (e.g., relays).

sweep Outer dial on face.

tachometer Scale to measure speed over a fixed course. Start the chronograph when crossing the starting line and stop it when the finish line is crossed. The sweep second hand will show the exact speed in miles per hour in the tachometer scale, which is based on a measured mile.

real time Reporting of an event as it happens, or computation of data as results come in, with nearly instantaneous readout.

microsecond (μs) Millionth of a second.

millisecond (ms. or msec.) Thousandth of a second.

RESPONSE TIMER

Measurement of reaction time to light, sound, and other signals—as shown by response through finger button, foot pedal, or other control—is made in milliseconds.

CINEMATOGRAPHY

Studies of human physical activity in which tasks are planned ahead of time take the form of a scenario. Motion picture film or closed circuit television coverage of a subject as he performs in accordance with a time-lined schedule or as he reacts to unplanned contingencies provides a record of activities which can be viewed as

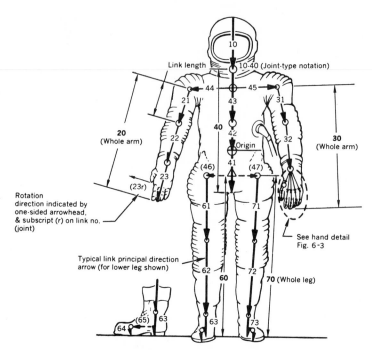

Fig. 6-2. Link diagram and numerical notation system. (From Roebuck, J. A., Jr.: NASA study, 1966.)

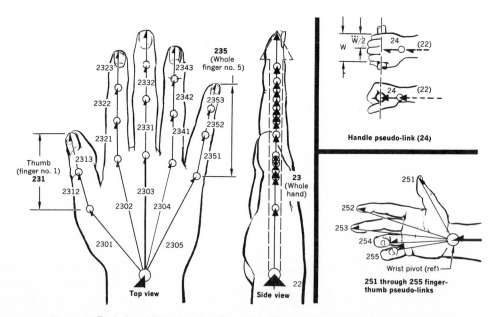

Fig. 6-3. Basic hand link details. (From Roebuck, J. A., Jr.: NASA study, 1966.)

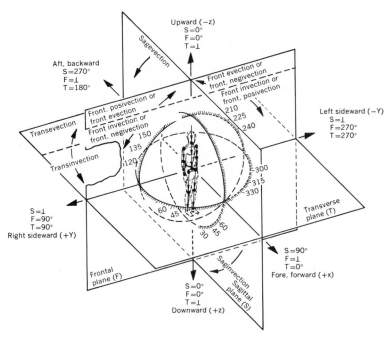

Fig. 6-4. Mobility terminology. Triplanar angular coordinate system. (From Roebuck, J. A., Jr.: NASA study, 1966.)

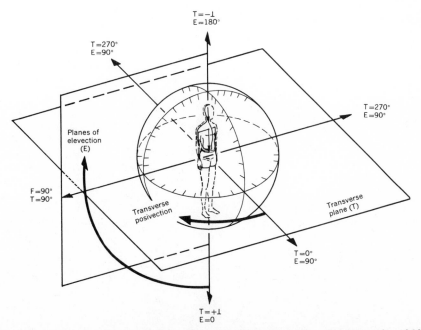

Fig. 6-5. Global coordinate system. (From Roebuck, J. A., Jr.: NASA study, 1966.)

a whole or as component parts, such as posture and movement. Through studies of this type, combined with other measurements such as oxygen uptake, heart rate, or body temperature, the physiological responses to the activity are described.

A 16 mm. motion picture camera is used to record the activity. Quantitative data reduction from motion picture photography is accomplished by projecting the film on a grid screen or microfilm reader or by using a motion analyzer that provides X-Y readout in the form of projected numerical display.

NUMERICAL SYSTEM OF MEASURING MOVEMENT

In order to describe every movement in terms of numbers, Roebuck developed a system in which the human body is considered as a series of mechanical linkages connected by joints, and the body's paths of motion in various directions and ranges as increasing or decreasing.

As shown in Fig. 6-2, the first digit for right limbs is even (2 or 6), and that for the left is odd (3 or 7). Segment numbers, with few exceptions, increase from head to toe.

The direction and range of movement are described in three planes, using 360-degree spherical scales as shown in Figs. 6-4 and 6-5. An example of numerical notation shorthand is given in Fig. 6-6. The zero direction for both the sagittal and frontal planes is always the same as that of link 41 (or link 40 when the trunk is considered as one single link).

MOVEMENT TERMINOLOGY

Except for the term "vection," used to describe rotary movements, root words are common to kinesiology and are shortened for use in combination to describe de-

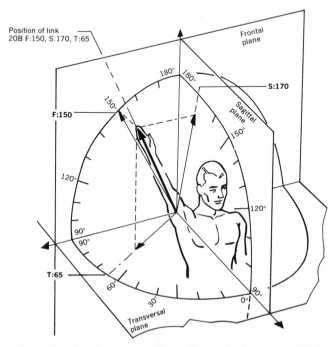

Fig. 6-6. Example of shorthand notation. (From Roebuck, J. A., Jr.: NASA study, 1966.)

creasing and increasing angular readings as movements progress. The following set of words describe all mobility performances. With these the exercise physiologist can relate the phenomena of his discipline, such as strength and metabolic requirements, to movements described precisely in terms of their type and direction.

1. Terms denoting type of movement

a. Vection (vek′shun)	Pivoting or revolving a link director (the principal director unless otherwise noted), or its projection on a principal plane, about an axis perpendicular to itself
b. Rotation	A rotary movement of a link about its major axis, or principal director. Described as an angular direction change (vection) of the rotary director
c. Torsion	Twisting of a link about its major axis, described as an angular direction change (vection) of the rotary director assuming the tail of the principal director is fixed

2. Terms denoting direction of movement—single links

a. Posivection (pos′i-vek-shun)	Vection in any plane producing an increasing angular reading in that plane. The plane in which action is measured must be specified by a preceding term; i.e., frontal, sagittal, transversal
b. Negivection	Opposite of posivection
c. Positive rotation	As seen from the tail of the principal director, rotation resulting in clockwise vection of the rotary director
d. Negative rotation	Opposite to positive rotation
e. Positive torsion	As seen from the tail of the principal director, torsion resulting in clockwise vection of the rotary director
f. Negative torsion	Opposite to positive torsion

3. Terms denoting direction of movement—dual links

a. Frontevection (frunt′e-vek-shun)	As seen from the front, clockwise vection of the right limb together with counterclockwise vection of the left limb about axes perpendicular to the frontal plane
b. Frontinvection (frunt′in-vek-shun)	Opposite to frontevection
c. Sagevection (saj′e-vek-shun)	As seen from the right, counterclockwise vection of the limbs about an axis perpendicular to the sagittal plane
d. Saginvection (saj′in-vek-shun)	Opposite to sagevection
e. Transevection (trans′e-vek-shun)	As seen from above, clockwise vection of the right limb together with counterclockwise vection of the left limb about axes perpendicular to the transverse plane.
f. Transinvection (trans′in-vek-shun)	Opposite to transevection
g. Fronterotation (frunt′e-roh-tay-shun)	Frontevection of the rotary directors of the limbs. *Positive fronterotation* implies that the principal director is pointing in the positive X direction, or forward. *Negative fronterotation* implies that the principal director is pointing aft, or in the minus X direction
h. Frontinrotation (frunt′in-roh-tay-shun)	Opposite to fronterotation. Frontinvection of the rotary directors of the limbs. As in above, *positive* implies that the principal director points forward; *negative* implies that the principal director points aft
i. Sagerotation (saj′e-roh-tay-shun)	Sagevection of the rotary directors of dual links. *Positive* implies that the principal director of the right limb is pointing to the right, or in the positive Y direction, and opposite for the left limb. *Negative* implies that the right limb is pointing left and the left limb is pointing right
j. Saginrotation (saj′in-roh-tay-shun)	Saginvection of the rotary directors of dual links. The terms *positive* and *negative* apply as in sagerotation above

k. Transerotation (trans'e-roh-tay-shun)
Transevection of the rotary directors of the limbs. *Positive* implies that the principal director of the links points downward, in the direction of the plus **Z** axis, *negative* implies the opposite

l. Transinrotation (trans'in-roh-tay-shun)
Transinvection of the rotary directors of limbs. The terms *positive* and *negative* apply as in transerotation above

m. Frontetorsion (frunt'e-tor-shun)
Frontevection of the rotary directors of the limbs with the tail end of the principal directors held fixed. The terms *positive* and *negative* apply as for fronterotation

n. Frontintorsion (frunt'-in-tor-shun)
Opposite of frontetorsion

o. Sagetorsion (saj'e-tor-shun)
Sagevection of the rotary directors of the limbs with the tail end of the principal directors held fixed. The terms *positive* and *negative* apply as for sagerotation

p. Sagintorsion (saj'e-tor-shun)
Opposite of sagetorsion

q. Transetorsion (trans'e-tor-shun)
Transevection of the rotary directors of the limbs with the tail end of the principal directors held fixed. The terms *positive* and *negative* apply as for transerotation

r. Transintorsion (trans'in-tor-shun)
Opposite to transetorsion

4. Combinations

The major terms for dual links are formed by combining the three terms denoting type of movement with the following prefix elements indicating direction:

a. -E- A positive upward- or outward-tending movement (from the standard position) or any motion resulting in an increasing angular coordinate of the right limb
b. -IN- Opposite to -E-, an inward or downward movement
c., d., e. The first syllable of each of the names for the principal planes (front, sag, trans)

Additional necessary distinctions for attitude of the limbs when performing rotational and torsional movements are defined by the terms *positive* and *negative*, which also serve to indicate direction for single links.

Form 6 is provided for numerical description of movements.

FORM 6

Numerical description of movement

Subject _____ Date _____
　　　　　　Name

Action	Link and type of movement	Notation		
		Plane		
		Frontal	Sagittal	Transversal
Whole right arm (20) elevected (E) in frontal posivection 150 degrees (F:150), saginvection 170 degrees (S:170), and transinvection 65 degrees (T:65)	20 E	F:150	S:170	T:65

FORM 7

Movement behavior protocol—energy schema

Force	Locomotion							Body segments						
	Weak						Strong	Weak						Strong
	1	2	3	4	5	6	7	1	2	3	4	5	6	7

Time	Locomotion							Body segments						
	Slow						Fast	Slow						Fast
	1	2	3	4	5	6	7	1	2	3	4	5	6	7

Space	Locomotion							Body segments						
	Small						Large	Small						Large
	1	2	3	4	5	6	7	1	2	3	4	5	6	7

FORM 8

Movement behavior protocol—shape in space

	Body position	Locomotion	Body segments
Path	Curved 1 2 3 4 5 Straight 6 7	Indirect-curved 1 2 3 4 Direct-straight 5 6 7	Indirect-curved 1 2 3 4 Direct-straight 5 6 7
Direction	Backward 1 2 3 4 5 Forward 6 7	*Accent* — Backward 1 2 3 4 5 Forward 6 7	*Accent* — Backward 1 2 3 4 5 Forward 6 7
		Down 1 2 3 4 5 Up 6 7	Down 1 2 3 4 5 Up 6 7
		Turn left 1 2 3 4 5 Turn right 6 7	*Center body* — In 1 2 3 4 5 Out 6 7
			Unilateral 1 2 3 4 5 Bilateral 6 7
Level	Flexed 1 2 3 4 5 Extended 6 7	Low 1 2 3 4 5 High 6 7	Low 1 2 3 4 5 High 6 7

FORM 9

Movement behavior protocol—rhythm*

Burst (sudden movements with a follow-through; ballistic; energy released as a spring or elastic recoil)

Burst
1   2   3

   a. Time and force equal throughout, strong and fast

   b. Agonist motor units act synchronously, followed by relaxation; antagonist responds with a stretch reflex

   c. Sudden acceleration, followed by deceleration

   d. High freqeuency of motor unit response

Restrained (inhibited, held back or controlled movement)

Restrained
1   2   3

   a. Time and force unequal, strong and slow

   b. Agonist and antagonist muscles operate simultaneously, motor units synchronously

   c. Acceleration continues evenly but resisted from beginning to end

   d. Medium to high frequency of motor unit response

Undulate (gradually increasing and decreasing energy of short duration)

Undulate
1   2   3

   a. Time and force equal, weak and slow

   b. Agonist and antagonist contract reciprocally

   c. Gradually increasing and decreasing number of motor units operate asynchronously

   d. Low frequency of motor unit response

Sustained (continuous, even movement)

Sustained
1   2   3

   a. Equal time and force continued from beginning to end; energy released over longer time

   b. Constant asynchronous motor unit activity of agonists; relaxation of antagonists

   c. Acceleration continued evenly but not resisted

   d. Low frequency of motor unit response

*Rhythm of a movement from beginning to end. Degree of control or freedom of movement based upon the amount of force and speed (time), expressed in observable rhythmic patterns.

MOVEMENT BEHAVIOR

Forms for noting an individual's particular style of movement as the person performs any kind of motor act have been developed by Hunt (Forms 7 to 10*). The characteristic way in which the person moves from the onset to the termination of the act is numerically noted on the forms in terms of energy expended, the shape and direction the body takes, and the rhythm of the movement. These notations are summarized in a profile of movement behavior. When results are compared with the person's exercise history, they are found to correlate well with his movement interests and experiences. The protocol may be useful in determining the subject's aptitudes and potentialities.

These forms are not for use in describing a given motor act and do not rate the individual's skill.

The *energy schema* (Form 7) is used to note the force, time, and space employed, in terms of whether the locomotion and the body segment activity would be characterized as weak or strong, slow or fast, and small or large.

*Courtesy Valerie V. Hunt, Movement Behavior Laboratory, Department of Physical Education, University of California, Los Angeles.

FORM 10

Movement behavior protocol—profile*

Criteria: Variability—a wide range between high and low scores; *consistency*—
a narrow range between high and low scores.

Position—place of scores: low, middle, or high.

Tendency—mode or constant disposition of scores.

Variability

Consistency

_____

Position

_____

Tendency

---

*Patterns of *energy, shape,* and *rhythm.*

The *shape in space* protocol (Form 8) is used to describe the path, direction, and level of body positions, locomotion, and body segments.

The *rhythm* protocol (Form 9) is used to note whether the pattern of movement took the form of a burst or of a restrained, undulate, or sustained rhythm. Each of these types of rhythm is described on the form, and a 1, 2, 3 scale is provided for indicating the low, moderate, or high degree to which the rhythm pattern was exhibited.

The *profile* (Form 10) is used to summarize the dominant characteristics of a person's movement style, when notations are made of the energy, spatial shape, and rhythm from a sampling of work, play, and expressive gestures, a central tendency or mode emerges as a prevailing pattern. Such broad movement sampling provides a measure of the variability and consistency of style. A wide range of scores on items and between items (great variability) is indicative of extensive capabilities with widely varied movement interests. A narrow range of scores (high consistency) indicates limited movement capabilities and strongly channeled interests.

TAPPING TEST

The maximal frequency with which a finger can be tapped is a measure of the functional condition and fatigue of motor centers of the brain. Results are not influenced by peripheral factors such as circulation or metabolism.

Equipment

- ☐ Telegraphic key
- ☐ Telephone counter
- ☐ Stopwatch

Procedure

- [ ] At signal "go" subject taps the key as rapidly as possible until signal "stop" is given.
- [ ] Operator starts the stopwatch at the first tap and calls "stop" at the end of 10 seconds. Operator encourages the subject to tap as fast as possible during the 10-second tapping interval.
- [ ] Tapping score is read from the counter and divided by 10 to obtain the per second rate. Repeat three times and record the highest score.

FUSION FREQUENCY OF FLICKER (FFF)

The rate at which alternating periods of light and dark can be discriminated before "flicker" disappears, being replaced by a visual impression of uniform grayness, is a measure of the fatigue state of the visual (retino-cortical) center of the brain.

Equipment

- [ ] Electronic stroboscopic light tube equipped with frequency readout.

Procedure

- [ ] Subject in a darkened room is instructed to call out "yes" when flicker appears, and "no" when it disappears.
- [ ] Operator starts at frequency well within gray threshold and slowly decreases the rate until the subject calls out "yes." The threshold frequency at which flicker became apparent is recorded.
- [ ] This time starting with a slow rate (flicker obvious), the rate is increased until the subject calls out "no," indicating that flicker is no longer perceived. That threshold is recorded.
- [ ] The process of decreasing and increasing the rate of alternating light and dark is repeated as above until a consistent rate is achieved. Record this rate as the subject's FFF score.

Proficiency check

Task	Date completed	Instructor's initials
1. Measure response time.	————	————
2. Analyze a motion picture of an activity:		
a. Prepare a numerical description (Form 6)	————	————
b. Derive quantitative data (Figs. 6-2 to 6-6)	————	————
c. Summarize the performer's movement style (Form 10)	————	————
3. Measure tapping rate.	————	————
4. Measure fusion frequency of flicker.	————	————

Sample experiments

- [ ] Investigate the relationships between response time, speed of movement, and rate of tapping.
- [ ] Prepare a scenario of a sequence of physical movements, including projected time

lines. Compare the scenario with a cinematograph of the tasks performed in a real situation.

☐ Describe a movement, using a numerical system.

☐ Describe a subject's characteristic style of movement using the profile in Form 10.

☐ Study the effect of fatigue on the fusion frequency of flicker.

REFERENCE

Roebuck, J.: A system of notation and measurement for space suit mobility evaluation, Hum. Factors **10**:79, 1968.

SUGGESTED READING

Barrow, H., and McGee, R.: A practical approach to measurement in physical education, Philadelphia, 1964, Lea & Febiger.

Frankel, V.: Orthopaedic biomechanics—the application of engineering to the musculoskeletal system, Philadelphia, 1970, Lea & Febiger.

Mathews, D.: Measurement in physical education, Philadelphia, 1963, W. B. Saunders Co.

Meyers, C., and Blesh, T.: Measurement in physical education, New York, 1962, The Ronald Press Co.

Smithells, P., and Cameron, P.: Principles of evaluation in physical education, New York, 1962, Harper & Row, Publishers.

Tapla, E.: Bibliography on high speed photography, Rochester, N. Y., 1960-64, Eastman Kodak Co.

Waddell, J.: Photographic motion analysis, Chicago, Industrial Laboratories Publishing Co.

CHAPTER 7

EXERCISE ELECTROCARDIOGRAPHY (ECG OR EKG)

THEORY

Morehouse, L. E., and Miller, A. T., Jr.: Physiology of exercise, ed. 6, St. Louis, 1971, The C. V. Mosby Co., chaps. 2, 3, 10, 11, 12.

Åstrand, P-O., and Rodahl, K.: Textbook of work physiology, New York, 1970, McGraw-Hill Book Co., chap. 11.

The electrocardiogram, a graphic representation of the electrical forces produced by the heart, is used (1) to ascertain whether a subject is qualified to engage in strenuous exercise and (2) to monitor the subject's response to exercise.

For the first purpose a standard twelve-electrode system* is employed to examine the subject's heart rate, rhythm and wave form while he is at rest. An abnormal ECG at rest, or while standing after rest, is one of the rejection criteria listed in Chapter 2.

For the second purpose a single bipolar ECG (three-electrode system) is evaluated constantly during exercise stress. ECG indices of exercise limits also have been listed in Chapter 2. Constant monitoring is necessary because significant ECG changes may be present only during 5 to 10 beats.

Use of the three-electrode rather than the twelve-electrode system for constant monitoring requires little time to prepare the subject, gives good performance during muscular activity because there is less chance of motion artifact, and reduces the amount of ECG data without seriously affecting the yield of significant results.

The exercise ECG is used to determine if there is coronary insufficiency, a disproportion between coronary flow and the blood demands of the myocardium—a condition called *myocardial ischemia*. Ischemia is exacerbated by exercise and is documented by wave form changes in the ECG due to myocardial repolarization abnormalities.

ECG instrument

A hard-wire ECG instrument is preferred to telemetry in exercise studies because it is more likely to meet the performance criteria for research and diagnostic interpretation. Performance specifications for ECG recording and data acquisition systems are as follows:

☐ Heart rate range

From 40 to 220 beats per minute.

☐ Expected noise and noise levels

Hum. Up to 100 μV. rms.

Periodic low-frequency baseline shifts with a slope up to 1 mV. per second.

Random noise. In the band width of 0.1 to 100 Hz, 100 μV. rms.

---

*Detailed descriptions of procedures for obtaining twelve-lead ECGs are found in instruction manuals provided by equipment manufacturers, so will not be included here.

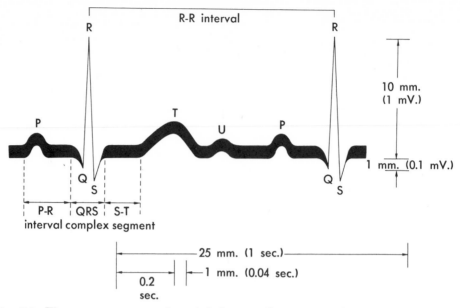

Fig. 7-1. The component parts of normal electrocardiogram wave forms are schematically represented, and the duration of the segments and intervals is indicated.

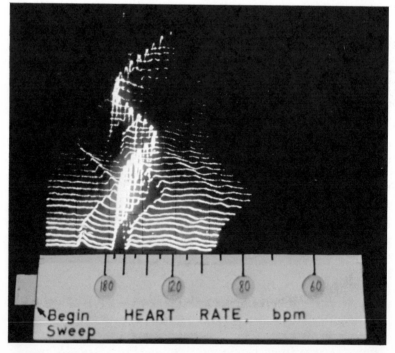

Fig. 7-2. ECG contourogram in continuous display mode. Image persistence fades so that when the sweep reaches the bottom of the CRT it can reset to the top, which by now has lost its earlier image. By varying the CRT persistence one can vary the number of previous ECG cycles available for reference at any one time. (Courtesy NASA.)

"Spikes" of short duration, sudden bursts of white noise, and other sudden transients deterimental to the measurement accuracy despite noise reduction methods. Portions of the signal affected should be recognized and rejected.

☐ Precision of amplitude meaurements

In the presence of noise the precision of amplitude measurements shall be 20 μV. or 10% of the signal amplitude, whichever is greater.

☐ Precision of interval measurements

Precision of interval measurements shall be 5 msec. for QRS interval and 20 msec. for other measured intervals.

Readout devices for ECG recording

☐ Cathode-ray oscilloscope (CRO). Cathode-ray vacuum tube with screen face filter providing short-persistence and long-persistence display.

☐ Direct writing recorder. Strip chart calibrated on a time base of 25 mm. per second (0.4 sec. per centimeter) and a sensitivity of 1 mV. per centimeter. For valid measurement of wave form intervals, the recorder should provide a paper speed of 50 mm. per second (0.2 sec. per centimeter). Standard ECG paper is used, which contains both time and amplitude scales.

☐ Magnetic tape recorder.

☐ Contourogram generator.

An improved ECG display for monitoring stress situations employs the use of real-time contourography. This technique—developed at the NASA Manned Spacecraft Center by Technology Incorporated scientists Golden, Mauldin, and Wolthuis— shows beat-by-beat changes in heart rate as well as changes in ECG wave form. By monitoring this type of contourogram (CRT), as illustrated in Fig. 7-2, the operator sees almost instantaneously the development of any unusual changes in the ECG. Polaroid photographs of the contourogram provide permanent records of the ECG events.

ECG CONFIGURATION

The resting heart is electrically polarized; the outside surface is positive, the inside negative. Each beat of the heart is initiated by a pacemaker, the sinoatrial (S-A) node, which starts a wave of negativity over the surfaces of the heart. This progressive depolarization moving over and through the heart precipitates contraction.

The electrical changes produced by the heart muscle depolarization are conducted to the body surface and can be detected there. When one electrode is placed near the apex of the heart and another sufficiently far away so that only voltage changes under the first will affect the recording, the waves of depolarization that move toward the near electrode will produce an upward deflection in the record, and the waves that recede will produce a downward deflection.

To interpret ECG wave forms, follow the electrical events as they produce the recording as depicted in Fig. 7-1 and tie them to the mechanical events in a cardiac cycle as follows:

☐ During total cardiac diastole there is no electrical activity and hence the record shows no deviation from the baseline. The heart is at rest.

☐ Atrial depolarization in the direction of the electrode produces an upward inscription. This is the P wave. The presence of P waves of normal size and shape preceding each QRS complex indicates that the excitation originates in the S-A node in a sinus rhythm and spreads through the atria. The atrial myocardium now starts to contract.

☐ There follows an atrioventricular (A-V) nodal delay that produces no electrical activity so the recording returns to the baseline and remains there until the onset of activity of the ventricles. This stay is the P-R interval. The period from the start of the P wave to the beginning of the QRS complex represents the time taken for the original impulse to spread through the atrial muscles and through the A-V node. Normally the P-R interval is between 0.12 and 0.20 second. If the P-R interval is prolonged, A-V nodal conduction is abnormal. If it is less than 0.12 second, accelerated conduction may be present. The atrial myocardium is contracting.

☐ After the A-V interval the course of activation crosses over the interventricular septum from left to right and thus away from the recording electrode, producing a downward Q wave as the right ventricular muscle mass is depolarized. The impulse, spreading down the bundle of His, descending through the left and right bundle branches, and reaching the terminal Purkinje fibers, brings the ventricular myocardium into contraction.

☐ As depolarization continues to the larger left ventricular muscle mass, it overlaps the electrical activity from the right ventricular muscle and the electrode "sees" only the wave of great magnitude moving toward it, the upward R wave. The entire ventricular myocardium is now contracting.

☐ As the ventricular activity ends in the posterobasal portion, the electrode "sees" the wave as receding and records a downward S wave, which returns to the baseline and exhibits a negative deflection of moderate amplitude. This QRS complex, the width between the onset of the Q wave and the completion of the S wave, represents the depolarization of the septum and the walls of the ventricles and normally requires between 0.10 and 0.12 second. If QRS is less than 0.10 second, the rhythm is supraventricular in origin. If greater than 0.12 second, the rhythm is either ventricular or supraventricular with aberrant conduction.

☐ There follows an S-T segment delay between the completion of depolarization and the repolarization (recovery) of ventricular muscles, which again produces no electrical activity so the recording again returns to baseline. The S-T segment may be depressed if the ventricle lacks oxygen (ischemia) or it may be elevated if the muscle is injured.

To measure S-T depression, three or more beats must be shown on a straight line, using P-R intervals as a base and drawing the line through the point of QRS onset of each. Express the displacement in millivolts (mV.) and millimeters (mm.). A stepwise procedure for measuring above amplitude changes is shown in Fig. 7-3.

Ominous rhythms

Paired prematurities, ectopic tachycardias, and prematurities of multifocal origins indicating myocardial irritability are not uncommon with exercise. They may be early signs of deterioration, which might be missed if an exercise test were not given.

PRELIMINARY PROCEDURES
Qualification for exercise ECG

Immediately before stress testing, whether the test is for evaluation of heart function or evaluation of the subject's capacity for endurance work, first ascertain that:

☐ Resting control twelve-lead ECG is normal.

☐ Recent medical examination and history show that the subject does not have an

Step 1. Draw isoelectric baseline

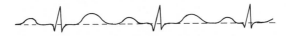

Step 2. Measure P, R, T, and U waves

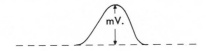

Step 3. Measure ST-J depression

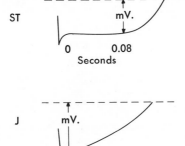

Fig. 7-3. Measurement of amplitude changes in ECG waves.

acute myocardial infarction (MI), has not had one in the past 6 weeks, and is not in preinfarctional state. (Review rejection criteria in Chapter 2.)

☐ Subject is not on therapy that could influence response to the test.

Preparation of electrode site

Use the method described in Chapter 4 for preparing the skin and applying electrode paste.

Attachment of ECG chest leads

For monitoring the subject's ECG response during exercise, select the chest lead with the tallest R wave, usually V5 or CM5 as shown in Fig. 7-4.

☐ Place the positive electrode at the standard V5 or C5 position on the left chest at the anterior axillary line and connect it to the left leg (LL) pin of the patient cable.

☐ Place the negative electrode over the manubrium of the sternum and connect it to the right arm (RA) pin of the patient cable.

☐ Place the ground electrode on the right chest, symmetrically opposite the positive electrode, and connect it to the right leg (RL) pin of the patient cable.

Safety check

Make sure that the defibrillator and other resuscitation equipment is ready and that the safety monitor and others involved in the test are familiar with routine and emergency procedures as outlined in Chapter 2.

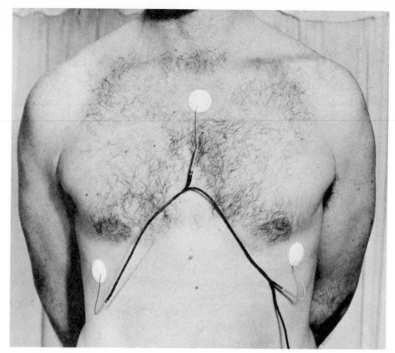

Fig. 7-4. CM5 electrode placement. The three electrodes placed on the manubrium sterni and left and right chest in the positions shown provide a scalar ECG that surveys the anterior aspect of the heart and presents an optimal display of anterior ischemia (S-T segment depression) during exercise. The electrode on the manubrium sterni is the reference (negative) electrode. The exploring (positive) electrode is placed on the left chest in the standard V5 or C5 position to obtain the highest R wave amplitude and strongest QRS and S-T display of the ECG. Placement of the right chest electrode opposite that on the left chest provides a good ground location and allows additional use for impedance pneumography (Chapter 10). (Courtesy NASA.)

Familiarization

☐ Familiarize the subject with the exercise device (bicycle, stepping bench, treadmill, or other ergometer as described in Chapter 14).

☐ Conduct a minute of low-level preliminary exercise.

☐ Monitor exercise and recovery.

Selection of exercise protocol

☐ Select a target heart rate (THR) by subtracting the subject's age from 200. Example, age 30:

$$THR = 200 - 30 = 170$$

☐ Establish a schedule of graded exercise as follows:

Time (minutes)	Exercise heart rate
0- 5	100
5-10	120
10-15	140
15-20	Target heart rate

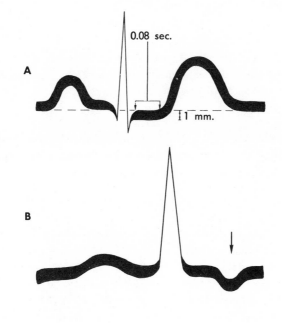

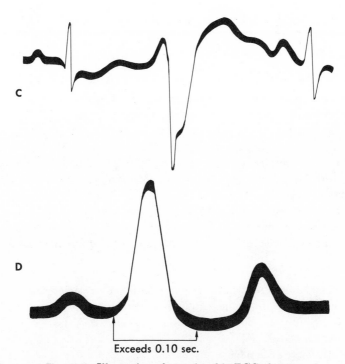

Fig. 7-5. Illustration of questionable ECG changes.

EXERCISE PROCEDURES
Instructions to subject

☐ Start exercising. If a bicycle ergometer is used, pedal at 60 r.p.m. or equivalent rate (Chapter 14).

☐ Report any and all symptoms immediately.

☐ Notify the operator of intention to stop exercise if premonition of exhaustion occurs before the end of the test.

Monitoring

☐ Observe the oscilloscopic display of the ECG continuously. Stop the exercise and instruct the subject to lie down at the first appearance of questionable ECG changes such as those shown in Fig. 7-5.

☐ Observe the appearance of the subject and question him regarding symptoms. Watch for end points of tolerance to exercise. Terminate the exercise at the earliest appearance of the first sign of poor tolerance. (See Chapter 2.)

☐ Observe the heart rate to be sure that the schedule of graded exercise is being followed. The subject's heart rate should be within 10 beats per minute of the scheduled exercise heart rate in about 2 minutes after the start of each level of graded exercise. During the last 2½ minutes at each level the heart rate should be within 6 beats per minute of the scheduled heart rate. If the exercise heart rate cannot be controlled within these limits by adjusting the work load, terminate the test after 5 minutes.

☐ Be ready to terminate exercise if anything develops with potential hazard to the subject (e.g., failure of the ECG monitoring system).

RECOVERY PROCEDURES
Instructions to subject

☐ Stop exercising. Stop breathing for a moment while the ECG is being recorded.

☐ Lie down on the examining table, face up.

☐ Lie quietly. Report any and all symptoms.

Recording

☐ As soon as the subject stops exercising get a good CM5 ECG tracing before he moves from the exercise device to the examining table.

☐ Commence the twelve-lead ECG as soon as the subject reclines on the table. The goal is to complete the recording of all leads within 30 seconds after exercise. It must be completed within 60 seconds after exercise to be acceptable.

☐ Record short CM5 strips at 30-second intervals. Observe oscilloscopic display of CM5 ECG during interim.

☐ Repeat twelve-lead ECG at 3 minutes after exercise.

☐ If all tracings are negative (Chapter 2), monitoring may be discontinued after 4 minutes. If tracing changed with exercise, continue monitoring until it is stable.

Recording conditions

In exercise electrocardiography, as in other physiological measurements of exercise responses, the following conditions should be noted:

☐ Temperature, if below 68° or above 74° F. (20° and 23° C., respectively).

☐ Humidity above 50%.

☐ Altitude above 5000 feet.

☐ Coffee and smoking within 2 hours of testing.

☐ Meals within 3 hours of testing.
☐ All drugs taken 1 week prior to testing.
☐ Exact time of ECG recording. If immediate postexercise recording is not completed within less than 30 seconds following cessation of exercise, note the exact time of the recording of each lead.
☐ Recorder speed (25 or 50 mm. per second).

INTERPRETATION AND REPORTING

Two kinds of statements may be made about ECG response to exercise: (1) whether or not an ischemic response occurred and (2) an estimation of the physical exercise tolerance.

Ischemic response

Report both subjective and ECG reactions. The ECG changes can be divided into primary, secondary, and tertiary. Only the primary change is an unqualified positive response.
☐ Primary. May be (1) horizontal depression of the S-T segment, greater than 0.10 mV. (1.0 mm.) for 0.08 second or more, having a flat or down-sloping configuration; (2) horizontal S-T segment depression induced by exercise and not relieved immediately by rest; or (3) junctional (J-point) depression with J down 0.10 mV. (1.0 mm.) or more together with dysrhythmias, bundle branch block (BBB), P wave depression, or T wave inversion.
☐ Secondary. Ventricular arrhythmia, intracardiac block.
☐ Tertiary. Supraventricular tachycardia, isolated T wave inversion, P wave changes.

Exercise tolerance (record on Form 11)

☐ State the heart rate at which the positive response occurred and describe its time-course (e.g., "became positive at exercise heart rate 120 and remained positive for 1 minute after exercise was terminated").
☐ Specify the work rate at the point of termination of the test.
☐ Estimate the relative exercise tolerance as follows:
  Normal: Completed exercise schedule without a sign of poor tolerance. Work rate at target heart rate exceeded 100 watts.
  Reduced: (1) Did not complete scheduled exercise, (2) completed exercise schedule with some discomfort, or (3) work at the target rate was 100 watts or below.

Proficiency check

Task	Date completed	Instructor's initials
1. Evaluate the performance of an ECG machine.	_____	_____
2. Connect a subject to an ECG machine using a V5 or CM5 bipolar electrode arrangement and obtain a sample record after exercise.	_____	_____
3. Identify the P, Q, R, S, T, and U segments of an ECG on a sample record.	_____	_____
4. Measure the wave heights of the above segments on a sample record.	_____	_____

(Continued.)

FORM 11

Exercise ECG report

Name_____ Social Security_____ Age____
        (First, middle initial, last)   (Number)   (Years)

Resting twelve-lead ECG

Negative _____

Date _____   Positive _____
    (Month, day, year)
                                Rhythm _____

                                Conduction _____

                                Ischemia _____

                                Myocardial infarction _____

                                Other _____

Exercise schedule		Exercise responses		
Duration (minutes)	**Heart rate (beats/min.)**	**Rhythm**	**Wave form changes (conduction, ischemia)**	**Symptoms**
0- 5	100			
5-10	120	_____	_____	_____
10-15	140	_____	_____	_____
15-20	_____	_____	_____	_____
	Target heart rate	_____	_____	_____

Reason for terminating test _____

Work rate at termination _____

Heart rate at termination _____

Ischemic response_____
                        (Primary, secondary, tertiary, none)

                    _____
                    (Heart rate at occurrence, and time-course)

Relative exercise tolerance _____
                            (Normal or reduced)

Comments: _____

_____

Interpretation: _____

_____

Test conducted by _____

Task	Date completed	Instructor's initials
5. Measure the wave intervals of the above segments on a sample record.	_____	_____
6. Describe an ischemic S-T segment response.	_____	_____

Sample experiments

Note the effects on the ECG tracing when the subject:

☐ Relaxes and tenses his muscles (differentiate ECG and EMG).

☐ Changes posture (lies, sits, bends forward, rests on side).

☐ Changes breathing pattern (holds breath, breathes deeply, hyperventilates).

☐ Smokes a cigarette with and without inhaling.

☐ Ingests ice water (cools the heart).

☐ Applies pressure on his eyeball.

☐ Pulls his hair, slaps the back of his hand.

☐ Performs an exercise test (use Form 11).

REFERENCE

Wolthuis, R., et al.: Real-time contourography—an improved electrocardiographic display, Aerospace Med. **41**:1247, 1970.

SUGGESTED READING

Bellet, S., et al.: Radioelectrocardiography during exercise in patients with angina pectoris, Circulation **25**:5, 1962.

Bellet, S., Roman, L., and Nichols, G.: Correlation of the electrocardiographic exercise test and blood cholesterol, Amer. J. Cardiol. **17**:43, 1966.

Berkson, D. M., Stamler, J., and Jackson, W.: The precordial electrocardiogram during and after strenuous exercise, Amer. J. Cardiol. **18**:43, 1966.

Blackburn, H., editor: Measurement in exercise electrocardiography, Proceedings of The Ernst Simonson Conference, Springfield, Ill., 1969, Charles C Thomas, Publisher.

Blackburn, H., et al.: Standardization of the exercise electrocardiogram. In Karvonen, M. J., and Barry, A. J., editors: Physical activity and the heart, Springfield, Ill., 1967, Charles C Thomas, Publisher.

Board of Regents: Instrumentation methods for physiological studies, vol. 1, Berkeley, June, 1964, The University of California Press.

Bruce, R. A.: Comparative prevalence of segmental ST depression after maximal exercise in healthy men in Seattle and Taipei. In Karvonen, M. J., and Barry, A. J., editors: Physical activity and the heart, Springfield, Ill., 1967, Charles C Thomas, Publisher.

Bruce, R. A., et al.: Quantitation of QRS and ST segment responses to exercise, Amer. Heart J. **71**:455, 1966.

Bruce R. A., and Hornsten, T.: Exercise stress testing in evaluation of patients with ischemic heart disease, Progr. Cardiovasc. Dis. **11**:371, 1969.

Bruce, R. A., and Yarnall, S.: Computer-aided diagnosis of cardiovascular disorders, J. Chronic Dis. **19**:473, 1966.

Caceres, C. A., and Dreifus, L. S.: Clinical electrocardiography and computers, New York, 1970, Academic Press.

Cady, L. D., Jr.: Computed relationship of standard electrocardiographic leads, Med. Res. Engin. **8**:37, May-June, 1969.

Cooper, K.: Guidelines in the management of the exercising patient, J.A.M.A. **211**:1663, 1970.

Doan, A., et al.: Myocardial ischemia after maximal exercise in healthy men, Amer. Heart J. **69**:11, 1965.

Hantzsche, K., and Dohrn, K.: The electrocardiogram before and after a marathon race, J. Sports Med. **6**:28, 1966.

Hartung, G.: Exercise electrocardiography using multi-point electrodes and computer smoothing techniques, Res. Quart. Amer. Ass. Health Phys. Educ. **41**:457, 1970.

Kossmann, C., et al.: Recommendations for standardization of leads and of specifications for instruments in electrocardiography and vectorcardiography, Circulation **35**:583, 1967.

Mason, R., Likar, I., and Ross, R.: New system of multiple leads in exercise electrocardiography, Circulation **30**:111, 1964.

Masters, A., Friedman, R., and Dack, S.: The electrocardiogram after standard exercise as a functional test of the heart, Amer. Heart J. **24**:777, 1942.

Mattingly, T.: The postexercise electrocardiogram—its value in the diagnosis and prognosis of coronary arterial disease, Amer. J. Cardiol. 9:395, 1962.

Most, A., et al.: Exercise ST changes in healthy men, Arch. Intern. Med. 121:22, 1968.

Passmore, R.: Energy, recreations, and the cardiac patient, Amer. Heart J. 71:579, 1966.

Rose, K., and Dunne, F.: A study of heart function in athletes by telemetered electrocardiography, Proceedings of the Fifth National Conference on the Medical Aspects of Sports, Chicago, 1964, American Medical Association.

Rose, K., Dunne, F., and Bargen, D.: Serum electrolyte relationship to electrocardiographic change in exercising athletes, J.A.M.A. 195:111, 1966.

Rosner, S., et al.: Computer analysis of the exercise electrocardiogram, Amer. J. Cardiol. 20:356, 1967.

Rowell, L., et al.: The physiologic fallacy of adjusting for body weight in performance of the Master two-step test, Amer. Heart J. 70:461, 1965.

Scherf, D., and Schaffer, A. I.: Review of recent advances—the electrocardiographic exercise test, Amer. Heart J. 43:927, 1952.

Simonson, E., and Keys, A.: Repeat variation of electrocardiogram, blood pressure and blood cholesterol within one hour and six months, Brit. Heart J. 32:660, 1970.

CHAPTER *8*

EXERCISE HEART RATE

THEORY

Morehouse, L. E., and Miller, A. T., Jr.: Physiology of exercise, ed. 6, St. Louis, 1971, The C. V. Mosby Co., chaps. 10, 11, 12.

Åstrand, P-O., and Rodahl, K.: Textbook of work physiology, New York, 1970, McGraw-Hill Book Co., chap. 6.

The heart rate or heart frequency (F_H)* is a simple and readily available index of cardiac stress, as it is directly proportional to the oxygen consumption of the heart. Activities that are most stressful to the heart are those in which highest heart rates are produced.

Individuals who can undertake intensive exercise with a small increase in heart rate are said to have a high degree of cardiovascular fitness. Environmental changes such as heat and altitude affect the response of the heart to exercise, and the heart rate resulting from the combined stress of exercise and environmental factors is a valid indicator of the total stress on the organism.

An exception to the uniform relation of heart rate to stress is the effect that emotional situations and mental loading have on the heart rate. In exercise studies, the emotional influences and mental loading should be avoided if the heart rate is employed to gauge the intensity of exertion. A method of documenting the effect of mental loading will be presented.

In experimenting with exercise heart rates without medical supervision, it is

---

*Also termed pulse rate, pulse frequency, and cardiac frequency, and all defined as the frequency of heartbeats in one minute.

Table 4. Heart rates in percentages of predicted maximum heart rates according to age

Age	Percentage of predicted maximum heart rate							
	50	60	65	70	75	85	90	100*
20	100	120	130	140	150	170	180	200
25	98	117	127	137	146	166	176	195
30	95	114	124	133	143	162	172	190
35	93	112	120	130	139	157	167	185
40	90	108	117	126	135	153	163	180
45	88	106	114	123	131	149	158	175
50	85	102	110	119	128	145	153	170
55	83	100	107	116	124	140	149	165
60	80	96	103	112	120	136	145	160

*The 100% values are population mean maximum heart rates.

FORM 12

Checklist of routine procedures in exercise studies

☐ Responsible investigator's outline for the project (Form 1) approved.

☐ Instructions to subjects issued.

☐ Appointment calendar for scheduling subjects is completed. When administered periodically, the test should be given at the same time of day.

☐ Rules of the laboratory reviewed and a safety checkout made. Resuscitation equipment ready and trained persons present. (See Chapter 2.)

☐ Subject's personal data (Form 2), health history, physical examination, exercise history, contraindications to exercise, and physician's consent are complete and satisfactory. There is no indication that the subject should be rejected (Chapter 2).

☐ Subject's consent (Form 3) is obtained.

☐ Environmental conditions (temperature, humidity, air movement) are recorded.

☐ Unless the test exercise is progressive in intensity, warm-up activities are allowed, which will promote relaxation and ease of movement, stretch muscles and their attachments, gradually increase heart rate, and induce slight sweating.

☐ During the test exercise the subject's responses are monitored continuously, and the activity is halted at the first sign of poor tolerance (Chapter 2). The subject's recovery following the test is monitored until his functions return to the near-resting state.

---

prudent, even though the subjects appeared to be healthy in a recent physical examination, to restrict the exertion to heart rates that are not higher than 75% of predicted maximum, or "critical," heart rate levels for the age of the subjects, as listed in Table 4. To further ensure safety and to guarantee reliable results, the guidelines for exercise studies are summarized in a checklist (Form 12).

FORMULA

$$\text{Heart rate in beats per minute} = \frac{60}{\text{R-R interval}} \qquad (4)$$

DEFINITION

representative R-R interval When rate is fluctuating, an R-R interval is considered to be representative when three successive R-R intervals within the period of interest are of the same duration. When the rate is sustained, an R-R interval is measured that is representative of the group.

MATERIALS

☐ Diary to record chronology of events

☐ Stopwatch with a sweep-second hand

☐ Stethoscope

☐ Small, portable ECG tape recorder

☐ Electrocardioscanner (rapid tape analyzer)

☐ Electrocardiocharter (records tracings of tape on ECG paper)

☐ Electrocardiograph*

☐ ECG paper marked into 3-inch intervals at the top margin

---

*Reliable and accurate over a pulse range of 40 to 220 per minute.

FORM 13

Record of heart rate by manual method

Resting

Heart rate
(beats/min.)

1-minute pulse count _____

30-second pulse count × 2 (trial 1) _____

30-second pulse count × 2 (trial 2) _____

15-second pulse count × 4 (trial 1) _____

15-second pulse count × 4 (trial 2) _____

20-beat heart rate determination (trial 1) _____

20-beat heart rate determination (trial 2) _____

6-second heart rate determination (trial 1) _____

6-second heart rate determination (trial 2) _____

Light exercise

6-second heart rate determination (trial 1) _____

6-second heart rate determination (trial 2) _____

Heavy exercise

6-second heart rate determination (trial 1) _____

6-second heart rate determination (trial 2) _____

Proficiency check

	Self (beats/min.)	ECG or other count (beats/min.)
15-second pulse count × 4	_____	_____
20-beat heart rate determination	_____	_____
6-second heart rate determination	_____	_____

☐ Competition, excited shouts to urge on, and strong incentives that preclude good exercise management are avoided.

☐ Silence is maintained during the test and recovery, and verbal or nonverbal communication (other than routine instructions to the subject) is prohibited. The subject is advised before the test that he is not to talk, as talking affects physiological responses.

☐ Medical review is required if poor responses (Chapter 2) are observed during exercise or recovery.

☐ Portable cardiotachometer*
☐ Time-elapse clock (synchronize ECG tape with diary)
☐ Cardiotachograph
☐ E-cell heartbeat counter
☐ Stepping benches (heights 12, 14, 16, 18, and 20 inches)
☐ Electronic metronome
☐ Cardiotachometer calibrator using tuning fork oscillator*

PROCEDURES
Location of arteries used for taking pulse by digital palpation

carotid artery In the neck, just to the side of the larynx (voice box). Palpate only one carotid artery on either side of the neck. Pressure on both carotids may reduce blood flow to the brain and cause fainting. Some individuals are highly sensitive to touch on the carotids, evoking reflexes that cause fainting due to rapid fall in blood pressure.

temporal artery In the head at the temple, usually along the hairline.

brachial artery In the upper arm, on the inside behind the biceps muscle and below the axilla (armpit).

radial artery In the wrist, on the palm side, directly in line with the base of the thumb.

Taking heart rate by palpation

In order to get a true heart rate for any activity the pulse should be counted during that activity when it has been maintained for several minutes.

☐ Before exercise, feel the pulse in the radial or carotid artery. Use the tips of the index and middle fingers—not the thumb, as it has a pulse of its own that can be confused with the subject's pulse.

☐ Start the stopwatch coincidentally with a pulse beat. Starting the count with a zero, count the pulses during a full minute while the subject is at rest. Record the heart rate (beats per minute) on Form 13.

☐ Again while the subject is at rest count the pulses for 30 seconds, counting the first pulse at zero, and multiply by 2 to obtain the per minute rate. Record the result on Form 13. This result should be the same as above, or slightly lower as the subject becomes familiar with the procedure.

☐ Next count the pulse for 15 seconds, multiply by 4, and record on Form 13. If the heart rate varies more than 3 beats per minute from the preceding 30-second count, repeat until the long and short counts tally. Always start the count with a zero.

☐ This time, while the subject remains at rest, use a stopwatch with a sweep-second hand and register the time required for 20 pulses to occur, counting the first pulse as zero. Refer to Table 5 to determine the per minute heart rate. Interpolate as necessary; for example, 13.8 seconds for 20 pulses equals a 70 per minute heart rate. Record on Form 13, compare with above values, and repeat if the deviation is greater than 3 beats per minute.

☐ While the subject is still at rest, make a 6-second heart rate determination by starting the count with a zero and counting the pulses for 6 seconds. Multiply by 10 to obtain the per minute rate. Enter the result on Form 13 and repeat until a comparative heart rate is obtained.

☐ Have the subject perform a light exercise such as stepping in place and repeat the above pulse-counting procedures during the third to fifth minute of activity. If it is not possible to feel the pulse during activity or to make a count because

---

*Reliable and accurate over a pulse range of 40 to 220 per minute.

Table 5. The 20-beat heart rate determination (0 to 20 beats)

Duration (seconds)	Heart rate	Duration (seconds)	Heart rate
16.0	33	10.8	120
15.6	40	10.4	127
15.2	47	10.0	133
14.8	53	9.6	140
14.4	60	9.2	147
14.0	67	8.8	153
13.6	73	8.4	160
13.2	80	8.0	167
12.8	87	7.6	173
12.4	93	7.2	180
12.0	100	6.8	187
11.6	107	6.4	193
11.2	113	6.0	200

of body movement, pause for a few seconds and make a 6-second heart rate determination. Start the count as soon as possible. Record results on Form 13.

☐ Repeat the above procedure with a heavier exercise. Record results on Form 13.

☐ Check proficiency against an ECG record, or by comparing with count made by another individual at the same time.

Taking heart rate by auscultation

The sound arising from the heartbeat may be counted as in the manual method. A stethoscope, used with the bell placed over the apex of the heart as shown in Fig. 8-1, aids in listening to the beat. The sounds arising from the heart aid the medical examiner in determining the physical condition of the subject.

Heart sounds may be amplified by using a piezoelectric microphone and a recorder with input impedance of at least 1 megohm.

Use of ECG recording for counting heart rate

Heart rate input signals during vigorous swimming and other activities in various environments can be obtained by using insulated electrode leads and gluing ECG silver or stainless steel disk electrodes onto a circular pad of neoprene. Electrodes are placed below the mamilla on the subject's chest wall between the fifth and sixth intercostal spaces and held in place by a neoprene vest. In ocean studies the salt water serves as a ground. The ECG leads are passed from the subject's back and allow freedom. Heart rates are obtained as follows:

☐ Record on a direct one-channel ECG writer with a paper speed of 25 mm. per second, using paper marked in 3-second intervals. At this paper speed a 3-inch strip the ECG tracing is the equivalent of a 3-second time interval.

☐ Count heart rate from R-R intervals in continuous periods of 6 seconds.

☐ Convert to beats per minute by multiplying the 6-second sum by 10 to get the rate per minute.

☐ As an alternate method, heart rate may be determined by measuring the time interval for each 20 cardiac cycles (Table 5).

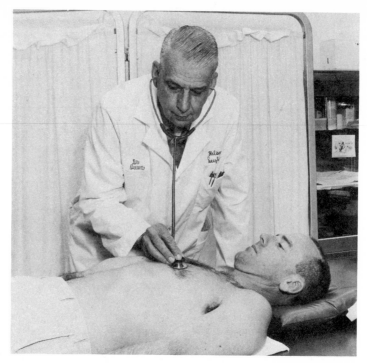

Fig. 8-1. Stethoscope placed over the apex of the heart to count heart rate and to determine subject's physical condition. (Courtesy NASA.)

☐ Classify resting heart rate as follows:

Bradycardia (slow rate)	Less than 60 beats per minute
Normal rate	Between 60 and 100 beats per minute
Tachycardia (fast rate)	More than 100 beats per minute

☐ Note the regularity. Ventricular rhythm is normal if difference in the time of successive R-R intervals varies less than 0.12 second per beat.

Immediate postexercise pulse count as a method of determining exercise heart rate

In the first 10 seconds after strenuous exercise (heart rate 160) is stopped, the heart rate counted from an ECG chart decreases about 5%. For many purposes, such as rating the intensity of exercise, this is an acceptable method of predicting the exercise heart rate.

When a method of palpation or auscultation is used, 4 seconds must be allowed for locating the pulse. Since it is nearly impossible to determine fractions of beats within intervals of measurement, it is more accurate to measure the length of time necessary for 20 beats to occur, as in Table 5. Errors in counting by palpation and auscultation are too high, even among experienced operators, to qualify these methods for anything more than rough estimates of exercise heart rate.

Photoelectric pulse pickup

A photoelectric cell may be placed over the ear, a nostril, a toe, or a finger as in Fig. 8-2.

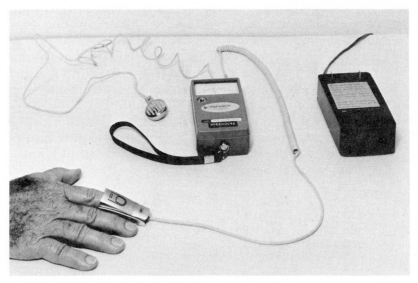

Fig. 8-2. Pulsemeter photocell on index finger senses changes in opacity, which are converted to "beep" signals at the speaker (left) and also to voltages that are displayed on the meter (center). The battery power of the system is recharged, using the charger (right). (Courtesy NASA.)

Heartbeat counter

Miniature, self-contained heartbeat recorders that can be carried in a pocket for 24 hours or more of usual activity, including physical exercise, consist of an ECG R wave amplifier, batteries, and counter mounted in a case.

The subject carries a data card and records at about hourly intervals while awake the time, the heartbeat count, and a short phrase describing his principal activity during each interval. A 10-minute "check run" is performed after each test to verify the performance of the counter.

DYNAMIC ELECTROCARDIOGRAPHY (DCG)

A small lightweight magnetic tape cassette combined with a miniaturized ECG provides a carry-around recorder for continuous acquisition of data regarding the cardiac cost of physical activities and the electrical activity of the heart while the subject carries on his usual daily routine. Recording at a low tape speed of 4 inches per minute provides a continuous record up to 30 hours. Replay at 15 inches per second enables readout of data in 8 minutes. The subject wearing the ECG recorder keeps a written log of each episode of elevated physical activity and any episode of "palpitation" or "dizzy spells." The extent and duration of episodes of increased activity are measured on the ECG record in terms of elevated heart rate. Scanning of the ECG record at the time of logged symptomatic episodes correlates symptoms and abnormalities.

The heart rate record is usually the end result of continuous long-term ECG monitoring of an active, unsupervised subject. Tracings of the ECG obtained on a strip chart or oscilloscope at 25 mm. per second sweep show what modifications in the ECG pattern have taken place. Modifications seen in the ECG wave forms may reflect axis shifts due to alterations in the position of the heart in relation to the electrodes, or they may be due to changes in the volume conductor characteristics of the body. Muscle artifacts due to straining, as well as the introduction of "noise" due to activation of electrical circuitry, frequently obliterate the ECG signal.

DYNAMIC CARDIOTACHOMETRY

When the normality of the electrical activity of the heart during vigorous activity has been assured by either an exercise ECG evaluation (Chapter 7) or a DCG evaluation, the subject's heart rate during exercise is monitored in order to assess the intensity of exertion. The heart rate is a more practical index of exercise stress than other parameters such as work performed or oxygen consumed.

The heart rate may be counted manually, or a portable lightweight cardio-

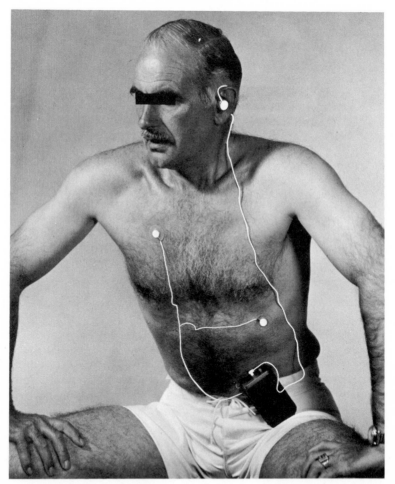

Fig. 8-3. CardioPacer. Chest electrodes lead heart's electrical impulses to pocket-sized unit which converts impulses to an audible signal heard in the earphone. When the heart is beating slower than a preset zone, an audible signal is heard. When the heart rate is increased by exercise to the zone level, the audible signal disappears. This heart rate zone can be established as the individual's training heart rate for monitoring exercise response. Whenever the heart rate exceeds the "safety" zone, a distinctive loud warning tone is sounded. (Courtesy Physio-Metrics.)

tachometer such as the one shown in Fig. 8-2 may be used. The portable pocket-sized cardiotachometer contains a meter that displays an "averaged" heart rate in beats per minute. It may also contain an audible signal device from which a short "beep" is heard for each heartbeat. An internal signal is provided for calibrating the meter. Remote monitoring is accomplished by telemetry.

One type of carry-around cardiotachometer, the CardioPacer shown in Fig. 8-3, delivers audio signals that indicate whether the exercise heart rate is above or below threshold limits of a preselected heart rate. The user is thus guided by the audio signal so that he maintains his exercising heart rate within chosen limits.

Heart rate monitor specifications

The equipment for monitoring heart rate during exercise is capable of monitoring rates between 40 and 220 beats per minute. Outputs of beat-by-beat and average rates over 10-second periods, or over 10 beats, with averaged values updated each beat, are manually selectable. Heart rate is displayed on a meter and recorded on paper tape operated at 1 mm. per second. An automatic alarm to indicate rates above a level manually set between 100 and 180 beats per minute can be provided. Built-in test signals are provided to calibrate outputs at 60, 120, and 180 beats per minute.

E-cell heartbeat counter

The problem of acquiring information on the physiological and environmental experience of subjects undertaking normal domestic duties has led to the development of "socially acceptable monitoring instruments (SAMI)," which are small in size and weight, consume little power, store simple data for many hours or days, do not interfere with normal activity or behavior, and are inexpensive. An example is a heartbeat counter SAMI that is a sensitive and reversible sealed miniature electro-plating cell (E-cell).* The charge passed through it at each heartbeat plates silver onto a gold electrode in proportion to heart frequency. A simple E-cell replay machine resets the cell in a few minutes by passing a reverse current, which gives a read-out of the stored charge and the simple total of heartbeats.

The heartbeat counter combined with an activity log provides a record of the "cardiac cost" of physical activity.

Cardiotachogram

One of the problems in assessing cardiac stress or energy cost of work on the basis of the exercise heart rate is to avoid the effects of mental loading. Sometimes this is impossible, and in such circumstances it is desirable to document the degree of the mental loading. This can be done by measuring the degree of variability of heart rate present during the work, since variability of heart rate is suppressed by mental loading.

Construct a cardiotachogram by making a histogram plot of beat-by-beat changes in pulse rate. When there is little or no mental loading, a marked change of rate of heartbeats is observed. If respiratory rhythm (Chapter 10) is plotted on the histogram, it may show that the heart rate fluctuation coincides with the respiratory rhythm when the subject is at rest.

When mental loading is increased, the histogram curve of heart rate changes

---

*Marketed by TEM Sales, Ltd., Gatwick Road, Crawley, Sussex, England.

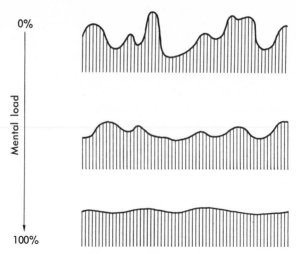

Fig. 8-4. Sample cardiotachogram illustrating changes in beat-by-beat heart rate.

flattens out. The degree of flattening can be scaled from perfectly flat (100%), extreme mental load, to the widest swings obtainable from the individual (0%), no mental load.

The histogram may be constructed from a standard electrocardiogram by measuring beat-to-beat intervals and plotting the time (in milliseconds) on a graph. This method may be accomplished electronically, using a cardiotachometer and a recorder that presents changes in beat-by-beat heart rate in the form of the cardiotachogram (Fig. 8-4).

Proficiency check

Task	Date completed	Instructor's initials
1. Derive heart rate from an ECG record.	_____	_____
2. Check count of heart rate by palpation against ECG record or cardiotachometer. Make comparative counts at rest and during exercise, using Form 13.	_____	_____
3. Classify a sample resting ECG record as to rate and regularity.	_____	_____
4. Calibrate and operate cardiotachometers and monitors.	_____	_____

Sample experiments

☐ Make a continuous record of the ECG (chart speed 25 mm. per second) on a subject during the transition from reclining rest to steady state exercise (bench stepping at a 120 beat per minute heart rate) through recovery (reclining) until heart rate returns to 10 beats above preexercise level. Tabulate (1) beat-by-beat heart rate, (2) heart rate averaged for each 6 seconds, (3) heart rate averaged from time intervals for each 20 beats, and (4) heart rate averaged for each 30 seconds. Plot the four determinations. Evaluate to select the method most representative of heart function.

☐ From the ECG record above, devise an original method of determining heart rate during transitions from rest to exercise and through recovery.

☐ Compare the effects on work heart rate of carrying a load in several positions (on the head, on the shoulders, and in the hands—both in front of the body and at the side).

☐ Record and explain the effects of fatigue, environmental temperature, cigarette smoking, and noise (cheering, music, conversation) on heart rate during an exercise.

☐ Compare the rates of pulse recovery from an exercise, measured for various postures (standing, sitting, reclining).

☐ Search for most rapid means of heart rate recovery from an exercise.

☐ Is heart rate recovery from exercise related to rate of rise of heart rate at the beginning of exercise?

☐ Correlate exercise heart rate scores with resting heart rates in subjects known to be in good, fair, and poor physical conditions.

☐ Compare age, sex, body weight, and physical condition differences in relation to preexercise, exercise, and postexercise heart rates.

☐ Chart repeated exercise results on one subject over a period of several weeks. Account for changes observed.

☐ Using heart rate as an index of cardiac stress, evaluate several activities, each continued for 5 minutes, and tabulate the immediate postexercise heart rates.

SUGGESTED READING

American Medical Association Committee on Exercise and Physical Fitness: Is your patient fit? J.A.M.A. 201:117, 1967.

Antel, J., and Cumming, G.: Effect of emotional stimulation on exercise heart rate, Res. Quart. Amer. Ass. Health Phys. Educ. 40:6, 1969.

Bashour, F. A., Jones, E., and Edmonson, R.: Cardiac arrhythmias in acute myocardial infarction. II. Incidence of the common arrhythmias with special reference to ventricular tachycardia, Dis. Chest 51:520, 1967.

Brouha, L.: Physiology in industry—evaluation of industrial stresses by the physiological reactions of the worker, ed. 2, New York, 1967, Pergamon Press, Inc.

Burton, A.: The importance of the size and shape of the heart. In Rosenbaum, F., and Belknap, E., editors: Work and the heart, New York, 1959, Paul B. Hoeber, Inc.

Burton, A.: Hemodynamics and the physics of the circulation. In Ruch, T., and Fulton, J., editors: Medical physiology and biophysics, Philadelphia, 1961, W. B. Saunders Co.

Carver, R., and Winsmann, F.: Study of measurement and experimental design problems associated with the step test, J. Sports Med. 10:104, 1970.

Corday, E., et al.: Detection of phantom arrhythmias and evanescent electrocardiographic abnormalities, J.A.M.A. 193:417, 1965.

Dill, D. B., et al.: Work capacity in acute exposures to altitude, J. Appl. Physiol. 21: 1168, 1966.

Edholm, O.: The assessment of habitual activity. In Evang, K., and Andersen, K., editors: Physical activity in health and disease, Oslo, 1966, Oslo University Press.

Ekblom, B.: Effect of physical training in adolescent boys, J. Appl. Physiol. 27:350, 1969.

Faria, I.: Cardiovascular response to exercise as influenced by training of various intensities, Res. Quart. Amer. Ass. Health Phys. Educ. 41:44, 1970.

Gilson, J. S., Holter, N. J., and Glasscock, W. R.: Unusual QRS alterations seen in continuous electrocardiocorder recordings, Amer. Heart J. 69:41, 1965.

Glick, G., and Braunwald, E.: Relative roles of the sympathetic and parasympathetic nervous systems in the reflex control of heart rate, Circ. Res. 16:363, 1965.

Hamilton, L.: An instant heart rate monitor, J. Appl. Physiol. 24:585, 1968.

Harvey, V., and Scott, G.: The validity and reliability of a one-minute step test for women, J. Sports Med. 10:185, 1970.

Holter, N.: New method for heart studies, Science 134:1214, 1961.

Kurucz, R. L., Fox, E. L., and Mathews, D. K.: Construction of a submaximal cardiovascular step test, Res. Quart. Amer. Ass. Health Phys. Educ. 40:115, 1969.

McArdle, W. D., Zwiren, L., and Magel, J. R.: Validity of the postexercise heart rate as a means of estimating heart rate during work of various intensities, Res. Quart. Amer. Ass. Health Phys. Educ. **40**:523, 1969.

Montoye, H. J., Willis, P. W., III., and Cunningham, D. A.: Heart rate response to submaximal exercise—relation to age and sex, J. Geront. **23**:127, 1968.

Morgan, B.: Cardiac arrhythmias in premature infants, Pediatrics **35**:658, 1964.

Norland, C., and Semler, H.: Angina pectoris and arrhythmias documented by cardiac telemetry, J.A.M.A. **190**:115, 1964.

Sanders, J. S., and Martt, J. M.: Dynamic electrocardiography at high altitudes, Arch. Intern. Med. **118**:132, 1966.

Scholander, P. F., et al.: Circulatory adjustment in pearl divers, J. Appl. Physiol. **17**: 184, 1962.

Semler, H., and Lauer, L.: Telemetered electrocardiograms during cerebrovascular insufficiency, Northwest Med. **68**:548, 1969.

Shane, W., and Slinde, K.: Continuous ECG recording during free-fall parachuting, Aerospace Med. **39**:597, 1968.

Simons, D., and Johnson, R.: Heart rate patterns observed in medical monitoring, Aerospace Med. **36**:504, 1965.

Stenberg, J., et al.: Hemodynamic response to work with different muscle groups, sitting and supine, J. Appl. Physiol. **22**:61, 1967.

CHAPTER 9

ARTERIAL BLOOD PRESSURE

THEORY

Morehouse, L. E., and Miller, A. T., Jr.: Physiology of exercise, ed. 6, St. Louis, 1971, The C. V. Mosby Co., chaps. 10, 11, 12, 13.

Åstrand, P-O., and Rodahl, K.: Textbook of work physiology, New York, 1970, McGraw-Hill Book Co., chap. 6.

Blood pressure changes reflect the strain of load imposed on the cardiovascular system by exercise and changes in posture.

Blood flow within the blood vessels is inaudible; however, turbulent flow is detectable by auscultation. The various sounds that are heard as the brachial artery is occluded and opened provide indirect procedures for the measurement of blood pressure, which are painless, are innocuous, and represent no limitation on the active subject. Data from such indirect (arm cuff) procedures are comparative to direct measurements of pressure within the brachial artery while the subject is resting or standing quietly.

Indirect methods should measure pressure within 6 mm. Hg of simultaneous reading by direct method while the subject is at rest.

Such accuracy is not achieved by indirect procedures during exercise. If the exercise is strenuous, the systolic blood pressure taken by indirect methods usually underestimates the actual arterial pressure by 8 to 15 mm. Hg. Errors in taking diastolic pressure during exercise by indirect methods are even greater and sometimes pressures cannot be determined at all.

Indirect systolic blood pressure readings during recovery after exercise overestimate actual pressures by 16 to 38 mm. Hg. Furthermore, with the cessation of exercise the blood pressure falls abruptly because of the sudden withdrawal of the pumping action of the contracting muscles. After 5 to 10 seconds reflex vasoconstriction causes the arterial pressure to rise again. Thus attempts to measure exercise blood pressure by indirect methods during exercise or by direct postexercise arterial pressure readings are made only for gross interpretation.

TERMINOLOGY

blood pressure Pressure of the blood against the inner walls of the blood vessels, varying in different parts of the body during different phases of contraction of the heart.

systole Period of contraction of the heart during which blood is forced onward, causing the maximum blood pressure.

systolic blood pressure (indirect) Amount of air pressure within a pneumatic cuff that is sufficient to stop brachial artery flow.

diastole Period of relaxation and filling of the heart during which the minimum blood pressure occurs.

diastolic blood pressure (indirect) Amount of air pressure within a pneumatic cuff that is barely insufficient to restrict brachial artery flow.

pulse pressure Numerical difference between systolic and diastolic blood pressure readings.

mean arterial pressure ($\overline{P}_a$) Average of all pressures during the cardiac cycle. Obtained by dividing the pulse pressure by 3 and adding the result to the diastolic pressure.

sphygmomanometer (Greek: sphygmo = pulse + metron = measure). Instrument for measuring arterial pressure.

auscultation (Latin: auscultare = to listen to). Detection of sounds.

Doppler effect Apparent change in the frequency of sound waves when the distance between the source and the receiver is changing.

MATERIALS

☐ Sphygmomanometer: pneumatic compression bag and cuff connected to a mercury column or an aneroid barometer (manometer) calibrated in millimeters of mercury (mm. Hg), an inflating bulb or pump to create pressure, and a variable, controllable exhaust for deflation

☐ Stethoscope (auscultoscope): bell type

☐ Electronic stethoscope system consisting of a microphone, amplifier, transducer, and speaker for audio signals and a recorder for charting the sound waves

☐ Automatic blood pressure system

☐ Stopwatch

☐ Vessel of ice water

☐ Towels, paper or cloth

☐ Examining table or bed

Calibration of aneroid sphygmomanometer

Attach in series with a mercury manometer and increase pressure to 50, 100, 150, and 200 millimeters mercury (mm. Hg). Sphygmomanometer and mercury manometer readings should agree within 1 mm. Hg at all levels.

PROCEDURES

Arterial blood pressure measurements in a standing or sitting position are made with the left elbow halfway bent. The third intercostal space at the sternum, which is approximately opposite the position of the heart, is used as a reference level.

Auscultatory methods of determining blood pressure

Korotkoff method

Systolic blood pressure is determined from the first of the five Korotkoff sounds to be heard.

☐ Place the stethoscope bell gently below the break of the elbow at the antecubital notch over the distal brachial artery.

☐ Quickly inflate the cuff pressure about 30 mm. Hg above oscillation pressure, or to 200 mm. Hg.

☐ Slowly deflate the cuff so that the pressure falls below 40 mm. Hg and then rapidly and completely deflate.

The first Korotkoff sound is in the audible frequency range of 1600 to 2100 c.p.s. It is heard as a sharp "thud," caused by the sudden vibrating rush of blood through the artery, as a quantity of blood is ejected through the occlusion as the artery opens. This *first Korotkoff sound* is accepted as the index of systolic pressure.

In the *second Korotkoff sound* the pulse becomes more apparent and acquires a metallic tapping nature. In the *third Korotkoff sound* turbulence is reduced and a definite interruption between systole and diastole is observed. The *fourth Korotkoff sound* is muffling—a soft, blowing sound. This is the first diastolic point. The *fifth Korotkoff sound*, the last sound, is followed by total silence. This is the second diastolic point. This fifth or last sound occurs at 4 to 10 mm. Hg above the direct intraarterial diastolic end point and is the most accurate index of diastolic pressure.

Since the third, fourth, and fifth Korotkoff sounds may be in the 120 to 500 c.p.s. frequency range, the sounds tend to be muffled even when the examiner's hearing acuity is good. If his hearing capacity does not extend to the 120 to 500 c.p.s. frequency range, an examiner is not qualified to use auscultatory methods for determining diastolic blood pressure.

Rehfisch method

In the Rehfisch method the Korotkoff sounds are determined by increasing the arm cuff pressure, and the first sound heard on the rising pressure is taken as the diastolic pressure. When the sounds subside, the systolic pressure has occurred. In this method the early diastolic sounds may be obscured by the noise made by the air pumped into the air cuff.

Sources of error in blood pressure determinations

Variations in blood pressure measurements using auscultatory methods are caused by the following:
1. Instrument errors
    a. Inaccuracies of sphygmomanometer (calibration errors, hysteresis, etc.)
    b. Cuff width
    c. Cuff length
    d. Stethoscope response characteristics
2. Observer errors
    a. Mental concentration
    b. Reaction time
    c. Auditory acuity
    d. Confusion of auditory and visual cues
    e. Interpretation of sounds (training and experience)
    f. Rate of inflation
    g. Rate of deflation
    h. Prejudice (anticipation of reading in the region about 120/80 mm. Hg)
    i. Terminal digit preference
    j. Excessive or inadequate pressure applied to stethoscope
    k. Cuff placement and circumference adjustment
    l. Stethoscope placement
3. Background noise
4. Artifacts in arterial pressure due to compression of the brachial artery
5. Patient's condition (obesity, shock, various heart valvular conditions, etc.)

Nonauscultatory indirect methods

In the following methods the arterial pulse is observed at or below (away from the heart) the point of occlusion by an inflatable cuff. The assumption is that the occluding force and arterial pressures are nearly equal.

Oscillometric method

Visual recognition of return of blood, following occlusion, is made by study of the needle oscillation in an aneroid manometer. Above systolic pressure the needle oscillations, which are synchronous with the cardiac cycle, are less than 2 mm. Hg. As the cuff is slowly deflated, the oscillations suddenly increase perceptibly, to about 4

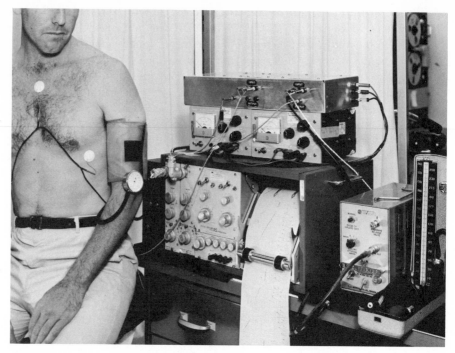

Fig. 9-1. Blood pressure recording. Blood pressure from cuff is recorded continuously on a strip chart. A contact microphone (not seen) is suspended in a pocket of the cuff over the brachial artery. After each automatic inflation and bleedoff of cuff pressure and the registration of systolic and diastolic blood pressures, the system is recycled. (Courtesy NASA.)

mm. Hg. This is the systolic pressure. The amplitude remains at this increased degree until the cuff is deflated to diastolic level, at which time the amplitude suddenly decreases to less than 2 mm. Hg.

This method is useful in environments with high noise levels.

Palpatory method

Return of pulse is noted in radial or popliteal artery, following obliteration by the cuff.

Flush method

Return of color as cuff is deflated is sometimes used for infants. Value may represent mean rather than maximum arterial pressure.

Automatic indirect method

The cuff is rapidly inflated and slowly deflated automatically on a previously programmed basis or on a manual signal, using an electric pump. Electronic auscultation methods using an encapsulated piezoelectric microphone and amplifier provide readouts of systolic (maximal) and diastolic (minimal) arterial pressures. Pressure is also charted on a recorder as in Fig. 9-1.

Ultrasonic sphygmomanometry, using the Doppler method (Fig. 9-2), has a slightly better capability than the microphone method of registering blood pressure—especially diastolic pressure—during exercise. Each reading is stored on a mercury manometer until another reading is made.

The method of measurement of one cycle of blood pressure from superimposed

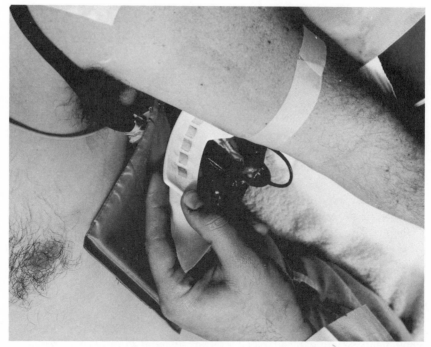

Fig. 9-2. Doppler sensor. Outer and center units transmit high-frequency sound pulses toward brachial artery. Intermediate units receive echo signals. As cuff pressure is reduced, systolic pressure opens brachial artery. Echo signals from movement of arterial wall produce Doppler effect that actuates recorder. (Courtesy NASA.)

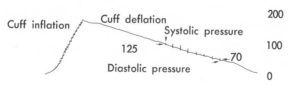

Fig. 9-3. Blood pressure measurement. Aneroid sphygmomanometer cuff pressure recording superimposed with Korotkoff's sounds on a strip chart. (Courtesy NASA.)

recordings of Korotkoff's sounds and sphygmomanometer cuff pressure is shown in Fig. 9-3.

During long-term monitoring an interval of at least a minute between readings (cuff completely deflated) prevents pooling of fluids in the arm.

Portable devices use compressed gas for cuff inflation and a tape recorder to store and play back the blood pressure signals.

As in auscultatory methods, the following conditions must be met in order to obtain reliable measurements: (1) patent brachial artery, (2) presence of pulsatile pressure waves, (3) nonmoving arm and relaxed hand, and (4) cuff at level with the heart.

Direct method of determining blood pressure

Direct determinations of blood pressure require the penetration of the bloodstream with foreign objects, thus inviting infection and discomfort. They are surgical techniques.

A strain-gauge pressure transducer of variable inductance is connected to an inserted catheter by an 18-gauge 1/16-inch wall plastic tube. Voltages are amplified and cathode-ray oscilloscope recorder tracings are used to obtain blood pressure readings expressed in mm. Hg.

SIGNIFICANCE OF BLOOD PRESSURE RESPONSES

A systolic pressure at rest above 170 mm. Hg suggests vascular hypertension. Strenuous exercise is contraindicated.

Failure during moderate exercise (heart rate 120 to 140 beats per minute) to increase and maintain systolic blood pressure 10 mm. Hg or more above resting level suggests inability of cardiovascular system to increase stroke volume in response to work. Strenuous exercise is contraindicated.

Diastolic pressures of 100 mm. Hg or higher are evidence of diastolic hypertension. Such values obtained during rest contraindicate strenuous exercise. (See Chapter 2.)

A sudden decrease in blood pressure during exercise denotes the onset of exhaustion. Terminate the work before the subject faints. See Chapter 2 for age-related end points of systolic and diastolic blood pressures during exercise.

HYMAN INDEX

Computation of the percent of change between recumbent mean blood pressure and quick-standing mean blood pressure demonstrates cardiovascular capability to accommodate to changes in body position. The postural mean blood pressure index (PMBPI) is obtained by calculating the mean blood pressure differences in the recumbent and quick-standing positions.

Procedure

☐ Subject lies quietly for 3 minutes. Measure systolic and diastolic blood pressures and compute recumbent mean blood pressure (RMBP).

$$RMBP = \frac{\text{Systolic blood pressure} - \text{Diastolic blood pressure}}{3} + \text{Diastolic blood pressure}$$

$$\text{Example: RMBP} = \frac{123 - 76}{3} + 76 = 91.7$$

☐ Subject stands quickly (on floor). Measure systolic and diastolic blood pressures and compute quick-standing mean blood pressure (QSMBP). Take the blood pressure within 10 seconds after standing.

$$QSMBP = \frac{\text{Systolic blood pressure} - \text{Diastolic blood pressure}}{3} + \text{Diastolic blood pressure}$$

$$\text{Example: QSMBP} = \frac{116 - 72}{3} + 72 = 86.7$$

☐ Compute the Hyman index.

$$PMBPI = \frac{QSMBP - RMBP}{QSMBP}$$

$$\text{Example: PMBPI} = \frac{91.7 - 86.7}{91.7} \times 100 = +5.46*$$

---

*Comparisons are made to RMBP. If QSMBP is greater than RMBP, as in the example, then PMBPI values will be positive.

Interpretation

$$\begin{aligned}
\text{Good} &= \text{Positive (+) values} \\
\text{Fair} &= 0.0\% \text{ to } -18.0\% \\
\text{Poor} &= \text{Below } -18.0\%
\end{aligned}$$

ORTHOSTATIC TOLERANCE

The effects of pooling of body fluids in the lower parts of the body during 5 minutes of quiet standing (measured by change in leg volume) are assessed by continuous surveillance of changes in blood pressure. As pooling occurs, cardiac output is lowered because of a reduction in venous return, and blood pressure falls. Before syncope occurs, the test is halted and the subject is assisted to the bed for recovery in the reclining position.

Procedure

- [ ] Subject lies quietly for 5 minutes.
- [ ] Subject stands motionless, leaning back against a wall, his heels 6 inches from the wall, for 5 minutes.
- [ ] Measure heart rate and systolic and diastolic blood pressures immediately after standing and each minute thereafter.
- [ ] Plot mathematical regression of heart rate and blood pressures against time.

Interpretation

A momentary fall in blood pressure is expected, due to diminished venous return when the subject stands up. Prompt compensatory vasoconstriction should return the blood pressure to slightly above resting level within 10 seconds. Orthostatic tolerance is poor if compensatory rise in blood pressure does not occur, if blood pressure rises above 20 mm. Hg higher than reclining, or if pressure falls during standing.

COLD PRESSOR TEST

- [ ] Record a series of systolic and diastolic blood pressures until stabilized at a low level.
- [ ] Thrust the free hand into a vessel of ice water (approximately 5° C.) to a depth well above the wrist.
- [ ] After a lapse of 10 seconds, repeat systolic and diastolic pressure recordings while the hand is held in the water.

Interpretation

If vasomotor centers of the brain are operating properly, both systolic and diastolic pressures will increase only to 10 mm. Hg. In hypertensive individuals the rise may be as much as 30 to 40 mm. Hg.

Proficiency check

Task	Date completed	Instructor's initials
1. Calibrate and operate an aneroid sphygmomanometer.	_____	_____
2. Identify the five Korotkoff sounds.	_____	_____
3. Compute the Hyman index, using values obtained from a subject.	_____	_____
4. Measure the orthostatic tolerance of a subject.	_____	_____
5. Measure the cold pressor response of a subject.	_____	_____

SAMPLE DATA SHEET

Name _____ Time _____

Sex _____ Age _____ Height _____ Weight _____

Method _____

Condition	Heart rate (beats/min.)	Blood pressures		Pulse pressure	Mean arterial pressure
		Systolic	Diastolic		
Recumbent for 3 minutes					
Quick-standing					
Recumbent for 5 minutes					
Leaning stand, immediate					
Leaning stand, 1 minute					
Leaning stand, 2 minutes					
Leaning stand, 3 minutes					
Leaning stand, 4 minutes					
Leaning stand, 5 minutes					
Seated for 5 minutes					
Hand in ice water 20 seconds					
Hand in ice water 40 seconds					
Hand in ice water 60 seconds					
Hand in ice water 80 seconds					
Hand in ice water 100 seconds					
Hand in ice water 120 seconds					
Recumbent for 5 minutes					
Seated, after bench-step 3 minutes					
Seated, after bench-step 6 minutes					
Seated, after bench-step 9 minutes					

Sample experiments

☐ Note the effect of exercise on blood pressure. Plot systolic and diastolic pressures every 3 minutes during recovery.

☐ Does the breathing pattern affect blood pressure readings?

☐ Note the effect of various postures on blood pressure.

☐ Relate blood pressure to age, sex, and body weight.

☐ Perform the cold pressor test on several subjects in varying degrees of cardiovascular condition as determined by the 1-minute step test.

☐ Relate resting (reclining) systolic and diastolic blood pressures to age, body weight, height, and sex.

☐ Determine effects of environmental temperature (hot and cold shower or bath) and body temperature on blood pressure, Hyman index, orthostatic tolerance, and cold pressor response.

☐ Plot diurnal variations in blood pressure by taking measurements every 4 hours for 48 hours. Note effects of sleep and other daily life activities.

☐ Observe effects of ingestion of food and fluid on blood pressure.

☐ Measure effects of various types and intensities of exercise on blood pressure.

☐ Study the effect of physical training on blood pressure and Hyman index.

☐ Study the effect of prolonged bed rest on blood pressure, Hyman index, orthostatic tolerance, and cold pressor response.

SUGGESTED READING

Altman, P., and Dittmer, D., editors: Respiration and circulation, Bethesda, Md., 1970, Federation of American Societies for Experimental Biology.

Astrand, I., Guharay, A., and Wahren, J.: Circulatory response to arm exercise with different arm positions, J. Appl. Physiol. 25:529, 1968.

Komi, P. V., et al.: Cardiorespiratory performance of Finnish university students, J. Sports Med. 10:6, 1970.

London, R., and London, S.: Blood pressure survey of physicians, J.A.M.A. 198:981, 1966.

London, S., and London, R.: Critique of indirect diastolic end point, Arch. Intern. Med. 119:39, 1967.

Marx, H., et al.: Maintenance of aortic pressure and total peripheral resistance during exercise in heat, J. Appl. Physiol. 22:519, 1967.

Reich, T., et al.: Effect of normo- and hyperbaric oxygenation on resting and post-exercise calf blood flow, J. Appl. Physiol. 28:275, 1970.

Schneider, R.: A fully automatic portable blood pressure recorder, J. Appl. Physiol. 24:115, 1968.

Stegall, H., Kardon, M., and Kemmerer, W.: Indirect measurement of arterial blood pressure by Doppler ultrasonic sphygmomanometry, J. Appl. Physiol. 25:793, 1968.

Steinberg, B., and London, S.: Automated blood pressure monitoring during surgical anesthesia, Anesthesiology 27:861, 1966.

Stromme, S. B., Kerem, D., and Elsner, R.: Diving bradycardia during rest and exercise and its relation to physical fitness, J. Appl. Physiol. 28:614, 1970.

Vogel, J., Hanse, J., and Harris, C.: Cardiovascular responses in man during exhaustive work at sea level and high altitudes, J. Appl. Physiol. 23:531, 1967.

Wyndham, C. H., et al.: A test of the effectiveness of acclimatization procedures in the gold mining industry, J. Appl. Physiol. 21:1589, 1966.

Yanoff, H.: Biomedical electronics, Philadelphia, 1965, F. A. Davis Co.

CHAPTER 10

SPIROMETRY

THEORY

Morehouse, L. E., and Miller, A. T., Jr.: Physiology of exercise, ed. 6, St. Louis, 1971, The C. V. Mosby Co., chaps. 15, 16.

Åstrand, P-O., and Rodahl, K.: Textbook of work physiology, New York, 1970, McGraw-Hill Book Co., chap. 7.

During exercise of progressive intensity pulmonary ventilation ($\dot{V}E$) increases in proportion to the increase in oxygen consumption ($\dot{V}o_2$) up to about 60% of $\dot{V}o_2$ maximum, after which $\dot{V}E$ increases at a relatively higher rate that is affected by increases in the depth and the frequency of breathing. Neither of these variables reaches the highest possible value in normal subjects; thus $\dot{V}E$ is not the limiting factor in hard, brief exercise. For the same reason, ventilation during exercise does not approach the vital capacity (VC) of the lungs. As may be expected, there is no significant correlation between $\dot{V}E$ or VC and athletic performance.

Respiratory rate (f)

Respiratory rate is a sensitive indicator of approaching exhaustion. A rate in excess of 45 breaths per minute is a sign (Chapter 2) that exercise should be terminated in older subjects. If the rate of respiration is rising inordinately, it is also a sign that the work is beyond the limit of compensation.

Training reduces the rate and depth of respiration at fixed work levels. To put it another way, training increases the amount of work that can be performed at former levels of respiratory rate and depth. The effect of training is to make breathing easier and to decrease the energy cost of respiration. This saving makes a significant contribution to the endurance for prolonged work.

Forced expiratory volume (FEV$_1$)

In disorders of lung function in which the airway is obstructed, the flow of air is restricted. Increased resistance affects both inspiratory and expiratory phases of respiration. The expiratory phase is most affected because it is the more passive and is dependent upon elastic recoil in the lung. Sensitive measures of lung obstruction are the 1-second forced expiratory volume (FEV_1), and the FEV_1 as a percentage of VC (FEV_1, % of VC).

Respiratory minute volume (MV)

During exercise the volume of expired air (VE) and the minute volume of ventilation (MV)—as factors that are to be related to metabolic, cardiovascular, or ergometric data—must be sampled under steady state conditions. The criterion of steady state is that three successive determinations do not vary more than 5%.

SPIROMETRY METHODS

Electronic methods using lightweight, low-friction arrangements for measuring lung volumes and flow (Fig. 10-1) are more accurate than methods using water

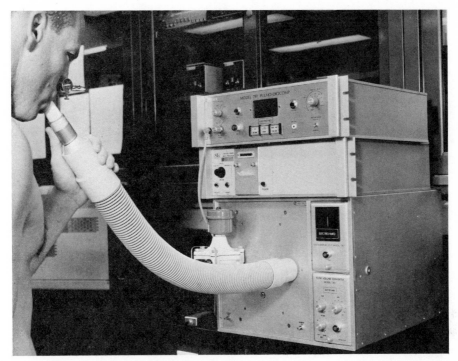

Fig. 10-1. Subject blowing into electronic Pulmanor respirometer. Values for flow rates, flow expiratory volumes, and timed vital capacity are printed out automatically on paper tape. (Courtesy NASA.)

manometers or gas collection bags. The greater resistance to breathing imposed by valves, tubing, and the weight of spirometer bells and gas collection bags affects the accuracy of determination of ventilation. Water spirometers do not operate correctly until the expired gas pressure is sufficient to move the cylinder. This delay is termed "lag time." Momentum of spirometer bells often produces "overshoot" or "undershoot." In bellows or bag type arrangements "ballooning" affects accuracy, as a result of the load imposed on the subject's lungs.

Electronic spirometers are calibrated against water spirometers, using air at the same temperature as the water. When water spirometers are filled slowly, the measures of volume are precise and constant.

Spirometric measures of *expired* lung volumes and flow are corrected to a standard body temperature (37° C.), pressure (760 mm. Hg), and saturation with water (47 mm. Hg P_{H_2O}). The abbreviation for this correction is BTPS.

Inspired volumes are corrected to a standard air temperature (0° C.), pressure (760 mm. Hg), and dry gas (0 mm. Hg P_{H_2O}). The abbreviation for this correction is STPD.

TERMINOLOGY

General variables

Symbol	Definition (specify dimensions and conditions)
V	Gas volume in general. Pressure, temperature, and percentage saturation with water vapor must be stated.

General variables—cont'd

Symbol	Definition
$\dot{V}$	Gas volume per unit time.
P	Gas pressure in general.
F	Fractional concentration in dry gas phase.
$\dot{Q}$	Volume flow of blood.
C	Concentration in blood phase.
f	Respiratory frequency—breaths per unit time.
R or RER	Respiratory exchange ratio. Ratio of the volumes of carbon dioxide and oxygen (volume CO_2/volume O_2), respectively, leaving and entering the body via the respiratory passages.
R.Q.	Respiratory quotient. Ratio of metabolic exchange of carbon dioxide and oxygen (volume CO_2/volume O_2).
D	Diffusing capacity in general. Volume per unit time per unit pressure difference.

Symbols for the gas phase

I	Inspired gas.
E	Expired gas.
A	Alveolar gas.
T	Tidal gas.
D	Dead space gas.
B	Barometric.

Symbols for the blood phase

b	Blood in general.
a	Arterial (specify exact location).
v	Venous (specify exact location).
c	Capillary (specify exact location).

Special symbols and abbreviations

$\overline{X}$	Dash above any symbol indicates a mean value.
$\dot{X}$	Dot above any symbol indicates a time derivative.
s	Subscript to denote the steady state.
STPD	Standard temperature, pressure, dry (0° C., 760 mm. Hg).
BTPS	Body temperature, pressure, saturated with water (37° C., 760 mm. Hg, 47 mm. Hg P_{H_2O}).
ATPD	Ambient temperature, pressure, dry.
ATPS	Ambient temperature, pressure, saturated with water.

Lung volumes and capacities

V_T	Tidal volume. Volume of gas inhaled or exhaled per respiratory cycle. Depth of breathing (milliliters per breath).
IRV	Inspiratory reserve volume. Maximum volume inhaled from end-tidal inhaled level.
ERV	Expiratory reserve volume. Maximum volume exhaled from end-tidal exhaled level.
RV	Residual volume. Volume of gas remaining in lungs after maximum exhalation.
MV	Respiratory minute volume. Total volume of gas inhaled and exhaled per minute (liters per minute).
$\dot{V}E$	Ventilation minute volume (expired) (liters per minute).
$\dot{V}_{O_2}$	Oxygen consumption. Oxygen consumed per unit time. Oxygen transfer rate from lungs to blood (liters per minute).
$\dot{V}_{CO_2}$	Carbon dioxide transfer rate from blood to lungs (liter per minute).
VC	Vital capacity. Maximum volume exhaled following maximum inhaled (liters).
IC	Inspiratory capacity. Maximum volume inhaled from the end-tidal exhaled level.

Lung volumes and capacities—cont'd

Symbol	Definition
FRC	Functional residual capacity. Volume of gas remaining at the end-tidal exhaled level (liters).
TLC	Total lung capacity. Total volume of gas contained in the lungs at the end of a maximal inspiration (liters).
FEV₁	Forced expiratory volume. The 1-second timed vital capacity.
MVV	Maximum voluntary ventilation. Maximum volume inhaled and exhaled in 15 seconds (liters per minute).

MATERIALS

☐ Electronic low-friction recording spirometer (Fig. 10-1)

☐ 120-liter, 350-liter, and 600-liter nonrecording gasometers (Tissot) (Fig. 10-2)

☐ 13.5-liter recording spirometer (Collins respirometer)

☐ 9-liter recording spirometer with soda lime canister and one-way valves removed

☐ Douglas bags (Collins) with respiratory valve assemblies (low-resistance Otis-McKerrow breathing valves; dead space 175 ml.) (Fig. 10-3)

☐ Stopwatch

☐ 80% ethyl alcohol

☐ Dry gas meter (American Meter Co. model 5-B-150, or tinned steel case dry test meter AS-8)

☐ Centigrade thermometer

☐ Barometer

☐ Body weight scales

☐ Body height stadiometer

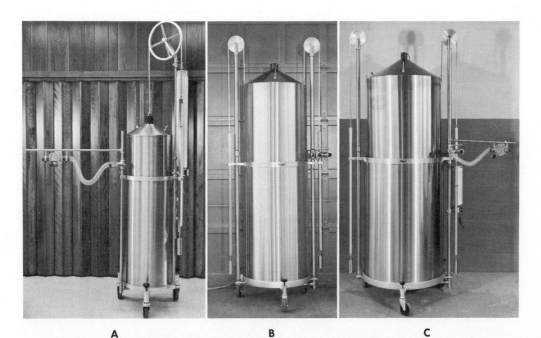

A　　　　　　　　**B**　　　　　　　　**C**

Fig. 10-2. A, 120-liter nonrecording gasometer; **B,** 350-liter nonrecording gasometer; and **C,** 600-liter nonrecording gasometer. (Courtesy Warren E. Collins, Inc., Braintree, Mass.)

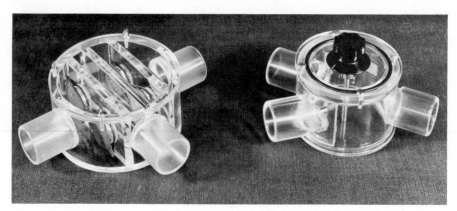

Fig. 10-3. Respiratory valve assemblies. (Courtesy Warren E. Collins, Inc., Braintree, Mass.)

Calibration of spirometers

The bell factor, K, is a constant, calculated as follows:

$$K = \pi r^2$$

SAMPLE DATA SHEET

Spirometer number	π*	r† (cm.)	r^2 (cm.²)	K‡ (ml./cm.)
000	3.14159	3.25	10.56	33.0

*π, or pi, is 3.14159.

†r = radius of spirometer bell.

‡K = bell factor (constant), which is stamped on spirometer. The ratio of cylinder volume to linear displacement (ml./cm.).

Capacity of spirometer

Volume = space (in a cylinder) occupied by matter:

$$V = \pi r^2 h; \; V = (\pi r^2)(h)$$

SAMPLE DATA SHEET

Spirometer number	K (ml./cm.)	h_{max}* (cm.)	V_{actual} (L.)	V_{rated} (L.)
000	33.0	32.8	135.34	135.00

*Linear indication of gas displacement of spirometer bell at maximum height.

STANDARDIZATION OF GAS VOLUMES

Gas volume reduction to standard atmospheric conditions (STPD)

Convert volume to value for barometric pressure of 760 mm. Hg, temperature $0°$ C., and dry gas ($STPD_{corr}$):

$$STPD_{corr} = \frac{P_B \text{ (mm. Hg)} - P_{H_2O} \text{ (mm. Hg)}}{760 \text{ (mm. Hg)}} \times \frac{273° \text{ K.}}{273° \text{ K.} + t° \text{ C.}} \quad (5)$$

where
760 (a constant) = barometric pressure at sea level
$273°$ K. = freezing point of water on Kelvin scale ($-0°$ C.)

SAMPLE DATA SHEET

Date, time	P_B (mm. Hg)*	P_{H_2O} (mm. Hg)†	t (° C.)‡	$STPD_{corr}$
1/1/72 0000	750.0	21.09	23.0	0.885

*P_B = ambient barometric pressure.

†P_{H_2O} = water vapor tension (i.e., pressure exerted by water vapor in collected gas sample).

‡t° C. = temperature of collected gas sample.

Gas volume reduction to conditions within the lungs (BTPS)

Calculate volume for body temperature ($37°$ C.), ambient barometric pressure, and air saturated with water vapor (BTPS):

$$BTPS_{corr} = \frac{273° \text{ K.} + 37° \text{ C.}}{273° \text{ K.} + t° \text{ C.}} \times \frac{P_B \text{ (mm. Hg)} - P_{H_2O} \text{ (mm. Hg)}}{P_B \text{ (mm. Hg)} - 47 \text{ (mm. Hg)}} \quad (6)$$

where
$273°$ = freezing point of water on Kelvin scale ($- 0°$ C.)
$37°$ (a constant) = body temperature
47 mm. Hg (a constant) = water vapor tension at $37°$ C.

SAMPLE DATA SHEET

Date, time	t° C.*	P_B (mm. Hg)†	P_{H_2O} (mm. Hg)‡	$BTPS_{corr}$
1/1/72 0000	23.0	750.0	21.08	1.086

*t° C. = temperature of collected gas sample.

†P_B = ambient barometric pressure.

‡P_{H_2O} = water vapor tension (i.e., pressure exerted by water vapor in collected gas sample).

Gas volume reduction to standard room air conditions (ATPD)

Calculate volume at 37° C. and the water vapor content of room air:

$$\text{ATPD}_{corr} = \frac{310}{273 + t° \text{ C.}_{amb}} \times \frac{P_B}{P_B - P_{W_{amb}}} \tag{7}$$

where

P_B = barometric pressure

P_w = water vapor pressure at 37° C., assuming 100% saturation = 477 mm. Hg

FORMULAS AND PROCEDURES
Vital capacity (VC)

Vital capacity is equal to the bell factor, K, multiplied by the spirometer displacement, h, and the BTPS correction.

$$VC = K \times h \times BTPS_{corr} \tag{8}$$

SAMPLE DATA SHEET

Subject	Condition	K (ml./mm.)	h (mm.)	t (° C.)	P_B (mm. Hg)	BTPS$_{corr}$	VC (ml.)	BSA (m.²)	VC/BSA (L./m.²)
Sample	Good	33	1150	23.0	250.0	1.086	4121.4	1.90	2.169

☐ Set the spirometer at zero.

☐ Inhale as deeply as possible, place the spirometer mouthpiece in the mouth, hold the nose, and exhale with maximum effort.

☐ Practice several times.

☐ Record three spirometer readings.

☐ Calculate VC (Formula 8) by multiplying the spirometer readings, h, by the constant, K, for the spirometer.

☐ Record gas temperature and ambient barometric pressure and correct for BTPS (Formula 6).

☐ Take the highest value as the subject's VC.

☐ From the nomogram (Fig. 10-4) determine the body surface area (BSA) of the subject. Express VC/BSA as liters per square meter of surface area.

One-second timed vital capacity (FEV₁)

Formula for forced expiratory volume in 1 second (FEV_1) is as follows:

$$FEV_1 = K \times h \times BTPS_{corr} \tag{9}$$

where FEV_1 = Forced expiratory volume in milliliters

K = bell factor in milliliters per millimeter

h = spirometer displacement in millimeters

BTPS = correction of volume to BTPS

☐ Use the same single-breath technique as in VC determination, a maximum exhalation following a maximum inhalation.

☐ If a kymograph is used, set the paper speed at 32 mm. per second.

DUBOIS BODY SURFACE CHART
Boothby and Sandiford

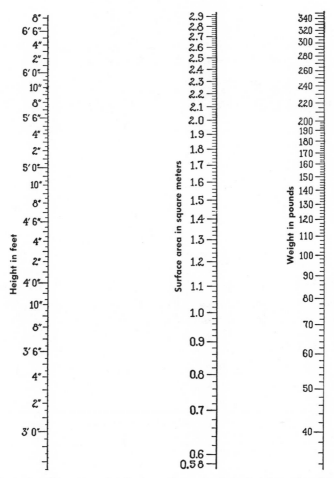

Fig. 10-4. Nomogram for computing body surface area from height and weight, for man.

☐ Measure the amount of air exhaled into the spirometer during the first second (FEV$_1$).

☐ Record the highest of three readings.

SAMPLE DATA SHEET

Subject	Condition	Kymograph speed (mm./sec.)	K (ml./mm.)	h (mm.)	BTPS$_{corr}$	FEV$_1$ (ml.)
Example	Good	32	33	87	1.086	3117.91

Percentage of timed vital capacity to total vital capacity (% VC$_{tot}$)

Formula for percentage follows:

$$\% \ VC_{tot} = \frac{FEV_1}{VC} \times 100 \qquad (10)$$

SAMPLE DATA SHEET

Subject	Condition	FEV$_1$ (ml.)	VC (ml.)	% VC$_{tot}$
Example	Good	3117.91	4121.4	75.7

Interpretation

A percentage VC$_{tot}$ of less than 72% indicates respiratory obstruction.

Maximum voluntary ventilation (MVV), or maximal breathing capacity (MBC)

- ☐ Clean the spirometer or install new disposable rebreathing liner.
- ☐ Insert mouthpiece and fasten noseclip.
- ☐ If a kymograph is used, set the paper speed at 32 mm. per second.
- ☐ Breathe as deeply and as rapidly as possible for 15 seconds.
- ☐ Measure the total volume of gas inhaled and exhaled during the time period, using the same techniques as in previous calculations. Convert to liters per minute.

SAMPLE DATA SHEET

Subject	Condition	Kymograph speed (mm./sec.)	V (L.)	t (sec.)	$\dot{V}$ (L./min.)	BTPS$_{corr}$	MVV (L./min.)
Example	Good	32	37.42	150	199.68	1.086	162.6

Minute ventilation (MV), nonrecording gasometer

Minute ventilation equals the height of gasometer excursion, h, multiplied by the bell factor, K, and the STPD correction, their product then being divided by minutes:

$$MV = \frac{h \times K \times STPD_{corr}}{minutes} \qquad (11)$$

☐ Record initial height of gasometer.

☐ Insert mouthpiece and fasten noseclip.

☐ Collect expired air in gasometer over a period of 1 minute, timed by a stopwatch, switching the air valve to the gasometer at the beginning and away from the gasometer at the end of the collection period. If an electric timer is used, the time switch can be arranged to operate simultaneously with the valve.

☐ Record the final height of the gasometer and subtract the initial height.

SAMPLE DATA SHEET

Subject	Condition	Bell height Initial (cm.)	Final (cm.)	F–I (cm.)	K (ml./ mm.)	V uncor- rected (L.)	STPD$_{corr}$	V cor- rected (L.)
Example	Good	52.4	77.2	24.8	33	8.19	0.885	7.2

Time (min.)	MV (L./min.)							
1.0	7.2							

Minute ventilation (MV), collection bag and gas meter

Minute ventilation equals the product of meter volume, V, and STPD, divided by minutes, t:

$$MV = \frac{V \times \text{STPD}_{corr}}{\text{minutes}} \tag{12}$$

☐ Roll bag tightly to expel all air.

☐ Record initial reading on gas meter.

☐ Insert mouthpiece and fasten noseclip.

☐ Collect expired air in bag over a period timed by a stopwatch, switching the air valve to the bag at the beginning, and away from the bag at the end of the collection period.

☐ Empty the bag completely into the gas meter.

☐ Record the temperature of the air in the gas meter and record the final reading on the gas meter.

SAMPLE DATA SHEET

Name	Condition	t (min.)	V (L.)	STPD$_{corr}$	V corrected (L.)	MV (L./min.)
Example	Good	0.50	4.073	0.885	3.60	7.20

Respiratory frequency (f)

Respiratory rate, or breaths per unit time (breaths per minute), can be counted by observing movements of the gas collection device. Direct observation of a subject's rib cage and abdominal movements to count f is made toward the rear of the subject.

At low rates of respiration under steady state conditions observations should cover a period of at least 4 minutes. Small inaccuracy in f measurements may introduce large errors in calculated indices. During vigorous exercise the observation should cover a full minute.

It is difficult for an individual to count his own breaths, as respiration becomes a voluntary function and he consciously takes over the control of both depth and rate.

Recording of f is accomplished by the use of an impedance pneumography (ZPG), discussed below, a plethysmograph or pneumograph using a belt attached to the chest, a thermistor bead mounted in front of the mouth in a mouthpiece or mask, or a heated pneumotachograph (Fleisch) that measures changes in respiratory air velocity by detecting the pressure loss at two points of a tapered cone.

If the pneumotachograph method is used to measure expired flow rates, the instrument should be calibrated with known volumes of air injected at the flow rates to be encountered during exercise studies. The range from rest to strenuous exercise is from 18 to 480 liters per minute.

Impedance pneumography (ZPG)

Common electrodes for ECG and respiration are provided by the three-electrode CM5 lead system shown in Fig. 7-3. The two chest electrodes receive an excitation signal of approximately 2 microamperes from a high-frequency square-wave oscillator. The impedance changes due to respiration cause minute changes in the amplitude of the signal voltage. The voltage variations are amplified and converted into a signal of approximately 0.1 volt for strip chart recording. The ZPG record is useful for quantitative measurement of both the rate and the depth of breathing during exercise.

Tidal volume (V$_T$)

The volume of gas inhaled or exhaled per breath, as computed from the following formula, is registered as milliliters per minute:

$$V_T = \frac{MV}{f} \tag{13}$$

Proficiency check

Task	Date completed	Instructor's initials
1. Record a 1-minute spirogram and measure:		
MV	_____	_____
f	_____	_____
2. Correct above values to BTPS.	_____	_____
	_____	_____
3. Record a forced vital capacity effort and measure:		
VC	_____	_____
FEV_1	_____	_____
4. Correct above values to BPTS.	_____	_____
5. Calibrate a spirometer.	_____	_____
6. Measure the gas capacity of a spirometer.	_____	_____
7. Convert above gas volume to STPD.	_____	_____

Sample experiments

☐ Relate vital capacity to the rate and depth and minute volume of respiration.

☐ Relate VC and FEV_1 to step test scores in subjects in poor and in excellent physical condition.

☐ Compare pulmonary ventilation measures among heavy smokers (more than 20 cigarettes per day) and nonsmokers.

☐ Study the acute effect of smoking on pulmonary ventilation.

☐ Observe the effect of fatigue of respiratory musculature (e.g., following endurance running) on maximum pulmonary ventilation capacity (VC and FEV_1).

☐ Measure the effect of posture (lying, sitting, standing erect, standing with shoulders rounded) on pulmonary ventilation.

☐ Study the acute and chronic effect of deep breathing exercises on pulmonary ventilation capacity.

☐ Correlate respiratory rate and minute volume with heart rate at progressive rates of exercise on a stepping bench.

☐ Is the period of respiratory recovery from exercise shortened or extended by periods of deep breathing or by periods of breath holding?

☐ Is there an anticipatory increase in ventilation rate or volume before exercise begins? Is this a conditioned response that can be extinguished?

SUGGESTED READING

Andrew, G., Guzman, C., and Becklake, M.: Effect of training on exercise output, J. Appl. Physiol. **21**:603, 1966.

Brown, J., and Shepard, R.: Some measurements of fitness in older female employees of a Toronto department store, Canad. Med. Ass. J. **97**:1208, 1967.

Consolazio, C. F., Johnson, R. E., and Pecora, L. J.: Physiological measurements of metabolic functions in man, New York, 1963, McGraw-Hill Book Co.

Cumming, G.: Correlation of athletic performance with pulmonary function in 13 to 17 year old boys and girls, Med. Sci. Sports **1**:140, 1969.

Douglas, F., and Becklake, M.: Effect of seasonal training on maximal cardiac output, J. Appl. Physiol. **25**:600, 1968.

Eldridge, F.: Anaerobic metabolism of the respiratory muscles, J. Appl. Physiol. **21**: 853, 1966.

Harden, K. A., et al.: Timed vital capacity in children, Amer. Rev. Resp. Dis. **91**:869, 1965.

Hermansen, L., and Saltin, B.: Oxygen uptake during maximal treadmill and bicycle exercise, J. Appl. Physiol. **26**:31, 1969.

Kasch, F., and Boyer, J., editors: Adult fitness—principles and practices, Greeley, Colo., 1968, All-American Productions & Publications.

Krumholz, R., Chevalier, R., and Ross, J.: A comparison of pulmonary compliance in young smokers and nonsmokers, Amer. Rev. Resp. Dis. 92:102, 1965.

Lamb, T., Anthonisen, N., and Tenney, S.: Controlled-frequency breathing during muscular exercise, J. Appl. Physiol. 20:244, 1965.

Luft, U.: Early detection of deteriorative trends in pulmonary function. In Marxer, W. L., and Cowgill, G. R.: The art of predictive medicine, Springfield, Ill., 1967, Charles C Thomas, Publisher.

Lynne-Davies, P., and Sproule, B.: Comparative studies of lung function in airway obstruction, Amer. Rev. Resp. Dis. 97:610, 1968.

Marsocci, V.: Proposal for an improved impedence pneumograph, Med. Biol. Engin. 5:333, 1967.

Ouellet, Y., Poh, S., and Becklake, M.: Circulatory factors limiting maximal aerobic exercise capacity, J. Appl. Physiol. 27:874, 1969.

Pappenheimer, J., et al.: Standardization of definitions and symbols in respiratory physiology, Fed. Proc. 9:602, 1950.

Pirnay, F., Deroanne, R., and Petit, J.: Maximal oxygen consumption in a hot environment, J. Appl. Physiol. 28:642, 1970.

Shields, J. L., et al.: Effects of altitude acclimatization on pulmonary function in man, J. Appl. Physiol. 25:606, 1968.

Sinning, W., and Adrian, M.: Cardiorespiratory changes in college women due to a season of competitive basketball, J. Appl. Physiol. 25:720, 1968.

Stromme, S. B., Kerem, D., and Elsner, R.: Diving bradycardia during rest and exercise and its relation to physical fitness, J. Appl. Physiol. 28:614, 1970.

Todorovic, B., Mihailovic, R., and Stojanovic, Z.: Comparison of some formulae for the prediction of vital capacity, J. Sports Med. 27:361, 1969.

Whipp, B. J., and Wasserman, K.: Alveolar-arterial gas tension differences during graded exercise, J. Appl. Physiol. 27:361, 1969.

CHAPTER 11

RESPIRATORY GAS ANALYSIS (SCHOLANDER)

THEORY

Morehouse, L. E., and Miller, A. T., Jr.: Physiology of exercise, ed. 6, St. Louis, 1971, The C. V. Mosby Co., chaps. 15, 16.

Åstrand, P-O., and Rodahl, K.: Textbook of work physiology, New York, 1970, McGraw-Hill Book Co., chap. 7.

Expired air from spirometers (Chapter 10) is analyzed chemically by the Scholander method (Fig. 11-1). An accurately calibrated micrometer is used to measure the absorption of carbon dioxide, oxygen, and nitrogen from a sample. A 0.5 ml. portion of a gas sample is introduced into a reaction chamber connected to the micrometer burette and is balanced, by an indicator drop in a capillary, against a compensating chamber (thermobarometer).

Absorbing fluids for carbon dioxide and oxygen are tilted into the reaction chamber without causing any change in the total liquid content of the system. The balance of the gas against the compensating chamber is maintained during the absorption of the gas by delivering mercury into the reaction chamber from the micrometer burette. Volumes are read in terms of micrometer divisions. The procedure requires less than 10 minutes and the accuracy of estimation is ± 0.015 vol. %.

MATERIALS
Apparatus

- [ ] Scholander apparatus*
- [ ] Agitator
- [ ] Vacuum discard system
- [ ] Erlenmeyer flask, large
- [ ] Glass stirring rod
- [ ] Narrow neck, screw cap bottles
- [ ] Syringe, calibrated tuberculin, needleless
- [ ] Syringe, 150 ml., fitted with a no. 24 needle
- [ ] Syringe, 8 ml., fitted with a no. 24 needle
- [ ] Syringe, 5 ml., fitted with a no. 24 needle
- [ ] Vial, 8 ml.
- [ ] Suction pipette
- [ ] Waste bottle
- [ ] Sampling tubes, Barcroft type, with tap and Hg reservoir
- [ ] Pipette, transfer, with rubber tip
- [ ] Pipette, capillary, with rubber tube

*Scholander apparatus is available from Otto K. Hebel, Scientific Instruments, 80 Swarthmore Ave., Rutledge, Pa.

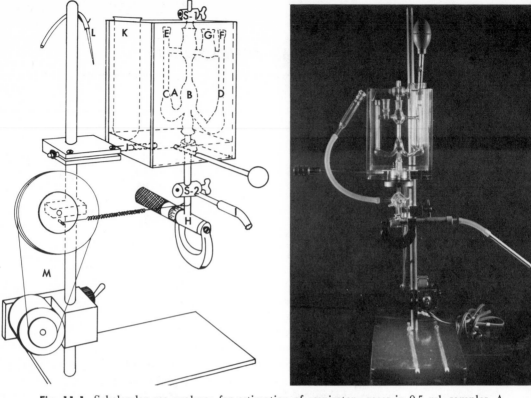

Fig. 11-1. Scholander gas analyzer for estimation of respiratory gases in 0.5 ml. samples. A reaction chamber unit consists of a compensating chamber (thermobarometer), *A;* a reaction chamber, *B,* and two side chambers for storing absorbents for carbon dioxide, *C,* and oxygen, *D.* The ends are closed with tight-fitting solid, vaccine bottle rubber stoppers, *E* and *F.* The compensating chamber can be closed with a stopcock, *S-1,* which between analyses is kept in a ground glass receptacle, *G.* A micrometer burette unit, *H,* is attached to a three-way stopcock, *S-2,* the side limb of which is connected with a mercury leveling bulb, *I.* A water bath unit rests on a rod that can be tilted by a handle, *J.* A 50 ml. centrifuge tube, *K,* suspended in the water bath is used for storing acid rinsing solution. Suction line, *L,* with a 15 ml. long fine-tipped capillary glass tube is used for sucking off waste fluids. Shaking device, *M,* consists of a motor that drives a counter wheel at a speed of 600 r.p.m. and moves an eccentric pin 1 cm. at the crankshaft to impart motion through a coil spring to the apparatus. (Courtesy Otto K. Hebel.)

Reagents

- ☐ Distilled water
- ☐ Anhydrous sodium sulfate (Na_2SO_4)
- ☐ Sulfuric acid, concentrated (sp. gr. 1.84)
- ☐ Glycerin
- ☐ Potassium dichromate ($K_2Cr_2O_7$)
- ☐ Potassium hydroxide (KOH)
- ☐ Sodium hydrosulfite ($Na_2S_2O_4$), powder
- ☐ Sodium anthraquinone β-sulfonate, powder
- ☐ Clarite X, or Picolite X, powdered
- ☐ Toluol
- ☐ Petrolatum or stopcock grease

Solutions, preparation and use

Acid rinsing solution

☐ Add 400 ml. of distilled water to a large Erlenmeyer flask.

☐ Dissolve 72 gm. of anhydrous sodium sulfate while continuously agitating.

☐ Deliver 1 ml. of concentrated sulfuric acid from a calibrated needleless tuberculin syringe.

☐ Deliver 21 ml. of glycerin from a needleless syringe.

☐ In 100 ml. of the above mixture dissolve 50 mg. of potassium dichromate. Save the remainder of the mixture, keeping it at room temperature, and add $K_2Cr_2O_7$ before each use.

☐ Store the 150 ml. of the dichromate solution in the acid rinse storage tube suspended in the water bath of the Scholander apparatus.

Clarite coating solutions

☐ Mix 1 gm. of Clarite X in 5 ml. of toluol. Mark "Clarite coating solution."

Water bath solution

☐ Pour distilled water at room temperature into the water bath to the neck of the compensating chamber. Add 5 ml. of ordinary bleach to inhibit microorganism growth.

Carbon dioxide (CO_2) absorbent

☐ In 100 ml. of distilled water dissolve 11 gm. of potassium hydroxide and 40 mg. of potassium dichromate. Store in narrow neck, screw cap bottle and mark "CO_2 absorbent."

Oxygen (O_2) absorbent

☐ In 100 ml. of distilled water, dissolve 6 gm. of potassium hydroxide. Store in a narrow neck, screw cap bottle and mark "Solution A."

☐ Prepare a powder mixture of 10 gm. of sodium hydrosulfite and 0.1 gm. of sodium anthraquinone β-sulfonate. Mark "Powder A." Store in a stoppered vessel and keep in a dark, dry place.

PROCEDURE
Filling side arm with carbon dioxide absorbent

☐ Connect the apparatus to the leveling bulb reaction chamber (stopcock *S-2* in position III), allowing the mercury to remain at the top of the analysis capillary.

☐ Insert the no. 24 needle of the empty syringe through the hole in the middle of the rubber stopper in the left side arm and remove the air until the mercury follows into the syringe.

☐ Remove the needle from the stopper while pressing on the side arm to prevent disconnecting apparatus.

☐ Charge left side with CO_2 absorbent. Remove all air bubbles.

☐ Press down on stopper and hold the side arm down while removing the needle so that joints are not loosened or disconnected.

☐ A leak in the vaccine bottle rubber stoppers sealing the side arms is a frequent cause of error. Replace stoppers after repeated puncturing and manipulation.

Filling side arm with oxygen absorbent

- ☐ Pour 0.6 gm. of powder A from a folded piece of paper into an 8 ml. vial. Add 5 ml. of solution A, close with a stopper, and dissolve anaerobically. Transfer O_2 absorbent immediately into an open 8 ml. syringe with attached no. 24 needle inserted into a soft rubber stopper.
- ☐ Quickly insert the plunger of the syringe, invert the syringe, remove the stopper, and expel excess air.
- ☐ Turn stopcock S-2 to position III and fill right side arm with O_2 absorbent, following above procedure for filling CO_2 sidearm. Exclude all bubbles.

Preparation for analysis

- ☐ Fill the compensating chamber up to the neck with acid rinsing solution.
- ☐ With stopcock S-2 in position III, opening into leveling bulb reaction chamber, draw the rinsing solution up and down just past the side arm openings by moving the leveling bulb (not the micrometer). Repeat washings at least four times, using a suction pipette to suck out the rinsing solution each time, and empty into waste bottle, continuing until the rinse solution remains yellow. Avoid sucking the rinse solution down through stopcock S-2, as it will remove the grease coating. Tie the leveling bulb with a string so that it cannot be lowered below the glass joint.

Introducing of sample

- ☐ Press out a small drop of mercury from a syringe into the bottom of the gas sampling tube (Barcroft), just above the tap. Hold the dry transfer pipette vertically and press the rubber tip firmly against the top of the gas sampling tube. Open the tap, gently blowing the mercury (Hg) drop into the pipette bulb and allowing some gas to bubble past it. Withdraw the pipette and, as the Hg drop starts to fall slowly down the tube, fit the rubber tip onto the top of the Scholander capillary in the compensating chamber.
- ☐ Screw the micrometer out until the gas sample and adjoining mercury meniscus reach the index mark in the middle of the capillary tube.
- ☐ Turn the stopcock to position II, connecting the micrometer and the leveling bulb, and adjust the micrometer to zero. This is the zero reading (V_0).
- ☐ Turn the stopcock to position I to connect the micrometer with the analysis chamber. Check to see that the meniscus is still at the capillary index mark.
- ☐ Screw micrometer evenly out to 70% of full scale. Screw micrometer back a few millimeters until Hg drop moves up, indicating slight positive pressure in chamber, which ensures against inward acid leak when transfer pipette is removed. Remove the pipette.
- ☐ Screw micrometer in, bringing about 2 mm. of the acid rinsing fluid into the top of the capillary tube.
- ☐ Suck away all the remains of the acid rinsing fluid from the compensating chamber, being careful not to withdraw the 2 mm. in the capillary tube.

Absorption of carbon dioxide

- ☐ Tilt the apparatus gently downward to the carbon dioxide absorbent side (left), admitting a small amount of the absorbent into the analysis chamber and covering the mercury with 1 mm. of the absorbent.
- ☐ Immediately tilt the apparatus back to horizontal. At the same time screw in the micrometer to compensate quickly for the rapid downward movement of the acid

---

FORM 14

Scholander data form

V_0	V_1	V_2	V_3	V_4	CO_2	O_2	N_2

---

drop in the capillary, occasioned by the carbon dioxide absorption. Tap stopcock *S-2* with finger to promote carbon dioxide absorption.

☐ Turn on the agitator for 5 seconds.

☐ Stir the water bath.

☐ Readjust the acid drop until lower meniscus is tangent with the index mark and read the micrometer again. This is micrometer reading V_2.

☐ Repeat tappings and readings until checks agree and record V_2 on Form 14.

Absorption of oxygen

☐ Repeat the above process for the oxygen absorbent, tilting the apparatus gently downward on the oxygen absorbent side (right), drawing in a small amount and covering the mercury with 1 mm. of the absorbent.

☐ Again tilt the apparatus back to horizontal and at the same time screw in the micrometer to compensate quickly for the downward movement of the acid drop as oxygen is absorbed.

☐ Turn on the agitator for 2 minutes, or until the absorption is completed, continuously screwing in the micrometer to compensate for oxygen absorption.

☐ Stir the water bath.

☐ Readjust the acid drop until lower meniscus is tangent with the index mark and read the micrometer. This is micrometer reading V_3. Repeat tappings and record V_3 on Form 14.

☐ Screw micrometer, drawing the 2 mm. acid drop down until the lower meniscus of the drop coincides with the index mark on the capillary. The 2 mm. drop separates outside air from the gas sample.

☐ Insert the tap of the open stopcock *S-1* in the top of the compensating chamber and close the stopcock.

☐ Stir the water bath.

☐ Lower the acid rinse drop to the bottom of the capillary tube to pick up any rinse adhering to sides.

☐ Raise the drop until the lower meniscus is on a tangent with the index mark. Note micrometer reading.

☐ Repeat until the meniscus and micrometer readings are constant. This micrometer reading is recorded as V_1 on Form 14.

☐ Turn stopcock $S\text{-}1$ to open the compensating chamber to the air and then transfer the tap to its socket, G.

☐ Screw the micrometer in until the indicator drop approaches the top of the capillary. Continue using the micrometer; suck the indicator drop off into the vacuum.

☐ Screw the micrometer in until the top of the absorbing solution in the chamber reaches the index mark in the capillary. Read the micrometer again. This is micrometer reading V_4. It should be within plus or minus 0.01 of 0.00 or the analysis is in error. An error of 0.005 (0.5 of a division on the micrometer) may be due to the elasticity of the side arm rubber stoppers.

Cleaning

☐ Fill the compensating chamber up to the neck with acid rinsing solution.

☐ Turn the three-way tap to connect the leveling bulb with the absorption chamber ($S\text{-}2$ in position III) and suck the absorbing solution into the vacuum discard, without allowing the absorbing solution to spill into the compensating chamber.

☐ Use the leveling bulb to draw acid rinse solution up and down four times just past the side arm openings. Rinse the reaction chamber and capillary in the same manner.

☐ Suck out the rinsing solution and repeat the rinse until the solution remains yellow.

☐ If the instrument is to be reused, it is now ready to be recharged by filling the side arms half full with respective absorbents.

Storing

☐ If the instrument is to be stored for 3 days or longer, suck out all water from the water bath and remove rinsing acid.

☐ Lower the mercury below the ground joint by lowering the reservoir. Remove the upper part of the apparatus from the ground joint. Cover mercury in reservoir with water to reduce toxic vapor.

☐ Hold apparatus over a beaker and remove the plugs to empty Hg and absorbents into the beaker.

☐ Wash thoroughly under a water tap and remove excess water by suction.

☐ Pour toluol into the compensating chamber, holding a finger in the lower end, and rinse through the middle with toluol. Repeat. Wash thoroughly with acetone and dry by suction.

☐ Coat the upper and lower thirds of the analysis capillary (i.e., about 1 cm.) with Clarite coating solution, using a capillary pipette. The middle third of the capillary is untouched by the Clarite coating solution. Rinse both ends with toluol to remove the Clarite coating solution. Dry with vacuum.

☐ Apply a slight suction to the apparatus overnight.

Calculations

$$CO_2 \text{ (ml./100 ml. original sample, dry)} = \frac{V_1 - V_2}{V_1 - V_4} \times 100 \qquad (14)$$

$$O_2 \text{ (ml./100 ml. original sample, dry)} = \frac{V_2 - V_3}{V_1 - V_4} \times 100 \qquad (15)$$

$$N_2 \text{ (ml./100 ml. original sample, dry)} = \frac{V_3}{V_1 - V_4} \times 100 \qquad (16)$$

Examples, where $V_0 = 0.002$, $V_1 = 10.000$, $V_2 = 9.637$, $V_3 = 8.112$, and $V_4 = 0.002$:

$$CO_2 \text{ (ml./100 ml., dry)} = \frac{10.000 - 9.637}{9.998} \times 100 = 3.6$$

$$O_2 \text{ (ml./100 ml., dry)} = \frac{9.637 - 8.112}{9.998} \times 100 = 15.3$$

$$N_2 \text{ (ml./100 ml., dry)} = \frac{8.112}{9.998} \times 100 = 81.1$$

The total of CO_2 plus O_2 plus N_2 should equal 100.

Proficiency check

Task	Date completed	Instructor's initials
Perform gas analysis of room air and a sample of expired air.	_____	_____

REFERENCE

Scholander, P. F.: Analyzer for accurate estimation of respiratory gases in one-half cubic centimeter samples, J. Biol. Chem. **167:**235, 1947.

SUGGESTED READING

Consolazio, C. F., Johnson, R. E., and Pecora, L. J.: Physiological measurements of metabolic functions in man, New York, 1963, McGraw-Hill Book Co.

CHAPTER 12

RESPIRATORY GAS EXCHANGE

THEORY

Morehouse, L. E., and Miller, A. T., Jr.: Physiology of execrise, ed. 6, St. Louis, 1971, The C. V. Mosby Co., chaps. 15, 16.

Åstrand, P-O., and Rodahl, K.: Textbook of work physiology, New York, 1970, McGraw-Hill Book Co., chap. 9, Appendix.

Estimation of heat production and metabolic rate by oxygen consumption during exercise is accomplished by analysis of respiratory gases. The closed-circuit method, employing a recording spirometer and measuring the rate of reduction of stored oxygen, is restricted to the mildest of activities such as quiet reclining, sitting, and standing.

Open-circuit methods, in which oxygen consumption is calculated from measurement of the volumes and partial pressures of inspired and expired respiratory gases, can be applied to the full range of physical activities. The standard laboratory procedure is the collection in bags or large spirometers (gasometers) of a series of gas samples for later analysis by Scholander or similar techniques (Chapter 11). With the subject under steady state conditions this procedure is highly accurate and is used to calibrate electronic devices.

Analysis of gas samples by mass spectrometry is accurate and fast. The paramagnetic oxygen analyzer, the gas chromatograph, and the oxygen electrode devices are costly, have slow response times, and are difficult to calibrate.

The need for continuous real-time determinations of metabolic rate in monitoring an exercising subject is being met by the development of oxygen consumption computers.* Although such a unit may contain a self-checking calibrator, the whole assembly must be periodically calibrated against standard laboratory procedures.

If standard gases are used to calibrate electronic devices, these must be checked by Scholander or similar precision techniques.

OXYGEN CONSUMPTION MEASUREMENT USING CLOSED-CIRCUIT RECORDING SPIROMETRY

Indirect calorimetry by closed-circuit recording spirometry employs a known initial amount of oxygen that is contained in a metal bell (Fig. 12-1). The bell is sealed by water at its base. The oxygen gas within the system does not interact with the atmosphere. One-way valves permit only unidirectional flow. In this demand system no pressure, save atmospheric, is placed around the gas.

The subject voluntarily inspires the gas from the bell and exhales it into a return line that incorporates a carbon dioxide absorber. A counterbalanced pulley arrangement causes the bell to respond to volumetric changes that occur with each

---

*Manufacturers: Technology/Versatronics, Inc., and Webb Associates.

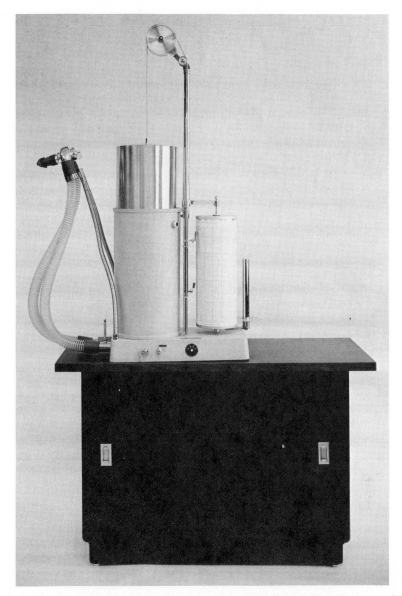

Fig. 12-1. Respirometer, 13.5-liter. (Courtesy Warren E. Collins, Inc., Braintree, Mass.)

inspiration and expiration. Over a given time period the oxygen uptake is represented by the reduction of gas in the bell.

The closed system, utilizing a simple spirometer, has the following disadvantages:

1. The CO_2 production cannot be registered; thus R.Q. cannot be obtained and
   meaningful energy cost determination is impossible.
2. The volume of O_2 in the bell is limited—a condition that limits the duration
   of the experiment.
3. During high flow rates, long tubing creates sufficient resistance to cause CO_2
   accumulation, bringing about an increase in minute volume, which falsifies
   results.
4. The system is subject to errors arising from leakage.

5. Erroneous results can occur, owing to displacement of end-tidal position or alterations in thoracic blood volume.

6. Volume errors from temperature changes may arise, particularly at high metabolic loads.

7. The apparatus is inadequate, in terms of resistance and inertia, at metabolic loads above 1 liter of oxygen per minute.

DEFINITIONS

small calorie (calorie with a small c) The amount of heat required to raise the temperature of one gram of water one degree Centigrade.

large calorie (Calorie with a capital C), or kilocalorie (kcal.) 1000 small calories.

FORMULA AND CALCULATIONS

To determine oxygen uptake ($\dot{V}_{O_2}$) use the following formula:

$$\dot{V}_{O_2} = V_i - V_f \tag{17}$$

where V_i = initial volume and V_f = final volume

Correct gas volume to standard temperature and pressure of a dry gas (STPD) as on p. 89.

Express in terms of large calories per square meter of surface area per hour (Cal./m.²/hr.).

Express as a function of lean body mass, if known.

OXYGEN CONSUMPTION MEASUREMENT USING OPEN-CIRCUIT SPIROMETRY

Gas distribution system

The air volume and concentration of O_2, CO_2, and N_2 in expired air are measured in the laboratory, using a system consisting of a mouthpiece and a one-way valve box (Collins triple-J) (Fig. 10-3) to provide routing of inspired gas to the subject and expired gas to the analyzers. The valve box is connected to the analyzers by a low-resistance, high-velocity gas meter and O_2 and CO_2 gas analyzers. The gas distribution system has minimal dead space volume, resistance to flow, and back pressure to the test subject.

In the field the expired gases are collected in bags (Douglas), meteorological balloons (Darex) or a portable gas meter that delivers air samples to collection bags.

After thorough mixing the gas contents of the bags are analyzed by passing dried samples through O_2 and CO_2 analyzers.

The collection bag system has the following disadvantages:

1. Only average values for a given interval of time can be obtained. Rapid changes in O_2 consumption and CO_2 production cannot be measured.

2. Bags, although assumed to be gas-tight, have a loss of gas concentration by diffusion.

3. Gas analysis by chemical means requires skill and is time-consuming.

4. Changes in respiratory gas exchange during exercise cannot be determined rapidly enough for real-time use in monitoring a subject's response to exercise.

Systems for on-line continuous determination of respiratory gas exchange during exercise utilize mass flow sensors, oxygen and carbon dioxide sensors, and computers (Fig. 12-2). The mass flow sensors are capable of monitoring expired gas with flow rates ($\dot{V}_E$) between 0 and 4000 ml. per second. The oxygen sensors are capable

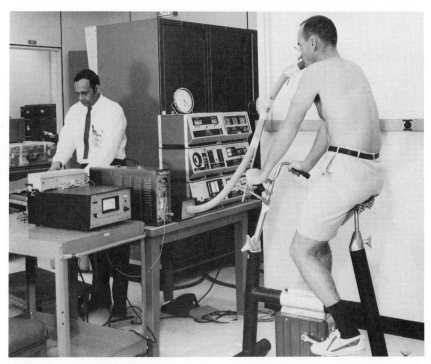

Fig. 12-2. Oxygen consumption computer. System for continuous computation and display of the amount of oxygen consumed during automatically timed 1-minute periods (by monitoring respired air) consists of a breathing mask and hose, mass flow meter, fan, oxygen polarographic sensor, heater to prevent condensation by maintaining the temperature of the sensor at 96° F., special-purpose analog computer, and two full-scale calibrators spanning the total range of applications from basal metabolism to maximal exercise. Assistant (left) collects bag samples for validation. (Courtesy NASA.)

of continuously indicating concentrations of oxygen in the range of 10 to 25% by volume; the carbon dioxide sensors indicate CO_2 in the range of 0.01 to 8%.

Sensor outputs indicating inspired and expired concentrations are fast and accurate enough to allow on-line computation of respiratory exchange ratio (R) by coupling the O_2 and CO_2 sensor outputs. The instrument range of R is 0 to 2.5. See p. 108 for differentiation of R.Q. and R.

Oxygen consumption (unit/time) $= \dot{V}_{O_2}$ (ml./min.) and may be determined from the nomogram of Dill and Fölling or computed from Formulas 18 or 19. Line charts for determining true $O_2\%$, R.Q., and STPD corrections are found in Consolazio, Johnson, and Pecora. Thus oxygen consumption may be calculated as below:

$$\dot{V}_{O_2} \text{ (ml./min.)}_{STPD} = \frac{MV_{(ml.)}}{100} \times \text{True } O_2 \qquad (18)$$

where true $O_2 = \%$ N_2 exhaled air $\times$ ratio of O_2/N_2 atmospheric air $- \%$ O_2 exhaled air by analysis and

STPD correction = standard condition (760 mm. Hg, 0° C., dry gas)

Or it may be calculated as follows:

$$\dot{V}_{O_2} \text{ (ml./min.)}_{STPD} = \frac{MV \text{ (ml.)}}{100} \times (\% \text{ } N_2 \text{ exhaled air} \times 0.265 - \% \text{ } O_2 \text{ exhaled air}) \quad (19)$$

Sample data sheets for use with these measurements are included below.

Oxygen consumption, open-circuit method

SAMPLE DATA SHEET

Name	Condition	Elapsed time (min.)	Bag no.	Volume uncorrected* (L.)	Gas temperature† (°C.)	P_B (mm. Hg)	STPD$_{corr}$
Example	Good	3.65	000	29.46	23	750.0	0.885

Volume corrected (L.)	MV (ml.)	Expired air analysis			True O_2‡ (%)	$\dot{V}_{O_2}$ (ml./min.)
		N_2 (%)	O_2 (%)	CO_2 (%)		
26.07	7142.5	79.0	16.8	4.2	4.14	295.7

*Dry gas meter volume.
†Dry gas meter temperature.
‡True oxygen % = % nitrogen exhaled × O_2/N_2 − % oxygen exhaled.

Respiratory quotient (R.Q.) and respiratory exchange ratio (R or RER)

During exercise in which the metabolic rate is not in a steady state, the ratio of volume CO_2/volume O_2 is expressed as the "respiratory exchange ratio," abbreviated as R or RER. The term "respiratory quotient," or R.Q., signifies a metabolic exchange of CO_2 and O_2 derived under conditions unaffected by hyperventilation or other non–steady state factors. See Formula 20:

$$\text{Respiratory quotient (R.Q.)} = \frac{\%\ CO_2\ \text{exhaled air} - 0.03}{\%\ N_2\ \text{exhaled air} \times 0.265 - \%\ O_2\ \text{exhaled air}} \quad (20)$$

where 0.03 = % CO_2 in atmospheric air
and 0.265 = ratio of % atmospheric O_2 (20.93) and % N_2 (79.04) in atmospheric air

R.Q. is measured at rest. During exercise, the solution to the above equation is termed the respiratory exchange ratio (R or RER).

OXYGEN CONSUMPTION EXPRESSED PER KILOGRAM OF BODY WEIGHT

Formula 21 corrects for differences in body mass when comparisons are made.

$$\dot{V}_{O_2}\ (\text{ml./kg./min.}) = \frac{\dot{V}_{O_2}\ (\text{ml./min.})}{\text{Wt. (kg.)}} \quad (21)$$

$$\text{Example: } \dot{V}_{O_2} = \frac{2500\ \text{ml./min.}}{53.5\ \text{kg.}} = 46.7$$

Materials

- ☐ Respirometer, 13.5-liter, closed-circuit, recording, with revolving drum and ink tracing; Ventilograph CO_2 absorber either liquid potassium hydroxide (KOH) or crystal calcium carbonate ($CaCO_3$); bell factor (πr^2) stamped on apparatus (Fig. 12-1)
- ☐ Oxygen, reagent grade
- ☐ Respirometer paper, lined; instructions usually seen along bottom edge of paper (e.g., Collins: "for 9-liter respirometer use above figures; for 13.5-liter respirometer double above figures")
- ☐ Mouthpiece for respirometer
- ☐ Centigrade thermometer, mounted in bell of respirometer
- ☐ Barometer, mercury or aneroid, sensitive to 0.5 mm. Hg
- ☐ Stopwatch
- ☐ Collection bag rack
- ☐ Back pack with hooks on upper corners to attach bags
- ☐ Gas collection assembly*:

  - ☐ Numbered collection bags of vinyl plastic or heavy-duty polyethylene, meteorological balloons or rubberized canvas (Douglas); capacity of Douglas bags, 125 liters and dimensions, 24 by 48 inches; inexpensive balloons with 200-liter capacity and 28 mm. necks also available†
  - ☐ Bag clamp
  - ☐ Wide-bore lightweight three-way tap with inner diameter of 1½ inches and flexible side arm tube or sampling nipple
  - ☐ Tubing, 3.18 cm. (1½ inches) inner diameter; hose length kept to minimum (50 cm.) to reduce dead air space; smallest inner diameter (i.d.) 28 mm.
  - ☐ Breathing valve (Otis-McKerrow, Collins triple-J, or Rudolph)—two-way, low-resistance, smallest i.d. 28 mm.
  - ☐ Mouthpiece and noseclip (face mask if nose is flat)

- ☐ Sampling bag or tube rack
- ☐ Numbered sampling bags or tubes, 1½-liter vinyl plastic bags, fitted with stopcocks or Spencer Wells forceps; or numbered 50 ml. syringes, lubricated with ethylene glycol or heavy paraffin oil; on syringes, a sampling nozzle consisting of a 2-inch length of pressure tubing with a screw clamp
- ☐ Bell spirometer (600-liter Tissot gasometer) or a high-precision, low-resistance dry gas meter (Parkinson-Cowan, Ltd., model CD4), with thermometer accurate to 0.2° C.
- ☐ 80% alcohol to sterilize mouthpieces
- ☐ Kofranyi-Michaelis (K-M) meter, or Max Planck respiration meter mounted on portable back pack, and plastic sampling bags
- ☐ O_2 and CO_2 gas analyzers—micro-Scholander, Haldane, gas partitioner (Fisher/Hamilton), gas chromatograph; paramagnetic O_2 analyzer (Beckman, Instrumentation Associates); infrared or thermal conductance CO_2 analyzer (Beckman, Cambridge)‡

---

*Flow resistance of assembly should not exceed 1 cm. H_2O at a flow rate of 100 liters per minute. Dead space area of breathing valve should not exceed 50 ml. Dead space of total assembly should be stated when reporting results.

†Available from Dewey & Almy, Cambridge, Mass.

‡The electronic (paramagnetic, polarographic, infrared, and mass spectrometric) O_2, CO_2 and N_2 analyzers and gas partitioners are calibrated by Scholander, Haldane, or gas chromatographic techniques.

☐ Mixing chamber of at least 5-liter capacity

Procedure

Calibration of gas meter

☐ Empty spirometer into gas meter at a steady rate of air flow. Agreement of spirometer and gas meter readings should be within ± 1%.

Measurement of resistance to flow

☐ Introduce water manometer in series with breathing valve, tubing, meter, and mixing chamber or containers.
☐ Adjust exhaust air flow to 400 L. per minute and read pressure (cm. H_2O).
☐ Repeat at flow rate of 3600 L. per minute and read pressure.
☐ Resistance to flow at either rate should not exceed 4 cm. H_2O.

Procedure, closed-circuit, bell spirometer method

☐ Face subject away from spirometer.
☐ Attach face mask or mouthpiece and noseclip, with valve in position for subject to breathe outside air.
☐ Check for leaks. Be sure noseclip is firmly attached.
☐ Fill bell with oxygen.
☐ Start the chart moving at 32 mm. per minute at beginning of inspiration by subject.
☐ Turn valve to position for subject to breathe spirometer gas.
☐ Collect a 5-minute sample.
☐ Record the spirometer temperature and the barometric pressure.
☐ Construct a base line parallel to reference lines on the chart.
☐ Draw lines perpendicular to the base line at the beginning and end of the 5-minute sample.
☐ Draw a sloping line connecting the majority of expiratory peaks.
☐ Measure the vertical displacement, "h," at the points where the lines perpendicular to the base line intersect with the slope line at the beginning and end of the sample period.
☐ Compute oxygen consumption rate as shown on p. 106.

Procedure, open-circuit method

☐ Subject wears a lightweight headgear that supports a mouthpiece and breathing valve connected to a container or mixing chamber.
☐ Subject breathes ambient air. Collect samples. Caution: do not assume partial pressures of atmospheric oxygen at 20.93%, carbon dioxide at 0.03% and nitrogen at 79.04%, even when outside air is used.
☐ Determine the volume of gas expired during sampling period by reading the gas meter and correcting for gas temperature and barometric pressure. Measure expired volume of bags or balloons by sucking the gas at a constant flow through the gas meter.
☐ If bags or balloons are used, the expired air is collected over 1-minute intervals. Note the number of each container and the time of each collection.
☐ Collect aliquot samples of expired air from the containers or mixing chamber in numbered 50 ml. syringes during the middle 30 seconds of each minute.
☐ Analyze gas samples for O_2 and CO_2.
☐ Compute the oxygen consumption rate as shown on p. 107.

Procedure, Douglas bag field method
CHECKING COLLECTION BAG FOR LEAKS

☐ Attach the bag to the outlet of a gas meter.
☐ Draw a measured volume of air and clamp off the neck of the bag.
☐ Place a 20-pound weight on the bag for an hour or more.
☐ Empty the contents back through the gas meter.
☐ Gas meter readings should be nearly the same.

RESPIRATORY GAS COLLECTION

☐ Empty collection bag completely of air by laying it flat on a surface with the exit open, rolling it up snugly, and clamping off the exit tube.
☐ Hang the bag on the rack or back pack and connect the exit tube to a three-way tap.
☐ Connect the tube from the mouth piece to the three-way tap. Tap is adjusted so that subject's air is going to the outside. Check for leaks around nose and mouth area while subject tries to blow air from nose.
☐ Commence air sample collection by simultaneously taking off the exit tube clamp, starting the timing watch, and turning the three-way tap so that all of the expired air goes into the bag.
☐ When the bag nears three fourths full (after about 10 minutes at rest and only 1 minute in maximal exercise), end the sample collection by noting the time to the nearest second and turning the three-way tap so that the subject breathes to the outside.
☐ Clamp off the neck of the bag, remove it from the rack, and mix the bag's contents by kneading it a few times.
☐ Connect the three-way tap to the gas meter and attach a sampling bag or syringe to the sampling nipple on the tap.
☐ Read V_1 from the gas meter.
☐ Open the three-way tap so contents of bag flow into the gas meter. Apply gentle pressure on the bag to press the gas out evenly.
☐ When the bag is half empty take a gas sample by flushing bag once before the collection. The syringe is drawn full and then emptied three times while the gas is flowing steadily. Finally fill the syringe, clamp off the rubber tube, and close the sampling nipple of the three-way tap. Take a duplicate sample.
☐ Pass the remainder of the air through the gas meter.
☐ Lay the bag flat and roll it up tightly from the bottom to pass all of the remaining gas through the meter.
☐ Clamp off the neck of the bag and take the final reading, V_2, on the gas meter.
☐ Make allowance for the amount of air drawn off when measuring the expiratory volume.
☐ Record the gas temperature in the meter to the nearest 0.5° C. and the barometric pressure to the nearest 0.5 mm. Hg.
☐ Convert the measured volume to volume at STPD.
☐ Analyze the gas sample within 3 hours to avoid loss of CO_2.
☐ Compute $\dot{V}O_{2STPD}$ (liters per minute).

CLEANUP PROCEDURE

☐ Review manufacturer's sterilization procedures.
☐ Wash mouthpiece with soap and water, rinse it in alcohol, and place it on a clean paper towel to dry.

☐ If noseclip has been used on a subject with nasal secretion, it should be washed and sterilized.

☐ Valves and connections should be washed with soap and water after use.

Proficiency check

Task	Date completed	Instructor's initials
1. Measure resistance to flow of spirometer system.	_____	_____
2. Measure oxygen consumption rate, using closed-circuit system.	_____	_____
3. From an open-circuit collection sample during exercise, compute:		
a. MV	_____	_____
b. % O_2	_____	_____
c. % CO_2	_____	_____
d. Oxygen consumption rate (ml./min.)	_____	_____
e. Carbon dioxide consumption rate (ml./min.)	_____	_____
f. R.Q. or RER	_____	_____
g. $\dot{V}_{O_2}$ (ml./kg./min.)	_____	_____
h. Oxygen pulse	_____	_____

Sample experiments

☐ Obtain the following data from a subject in the morning, after he has rested supine for 60 minutes, fasted for 12 hours, and has not been physically active or been drinking or smoking before test. Room temperature should be adjusted to 20° C.

Age _____ (yr.)

Sex _____

Height _____ (cm.)

Weight _____ (kg.)

Surface area _____ (m.²) (from Fig. 10-4)

Barometric pressure _____ (mm. Hg)

O_2 temperature _____ (°C.)

Correction factor (STPD) _____

Bell factor (K) _____ (ml./mm.)

Fall in spirometer bell in 6 minutes (h) _____ (mm.)

Uncorrected O_2 used in 6 minutes (K × h) _____ (ml.)

Corrected O_2 used per hour (K × h × 10 × STPD) _____ (L.)

Caloric equivalent of O_2 used ($\dot{V}_{O_2}$/hr. × 4.825) _____ (Cal./hr.)

Basal metabolic rate (BMR) _____ (Cal./hr./ m.²)

SAMPLE DATA SHEET

Name _____ Example _____

Social Security No. _____ 049-03-23-28 _____

Age _____ 24803 _____

Sex _____ Male _____

Condition _____ Good _____

Height _____ 176 cm. _____

Weight _____ 75.0 kg. _____

Date of examination _____ 1/1/72 _____

Place of examination _____ Exercise Laboratory _____

Barometric pressure _____ 750.0 mm. _____

Wet bulb (WB) temperature _____ 17° C. _____

Dry bulb (DB) temperature _____ 23° C. _____

$\dot{V}_{E_{ATPS}}$ (L./min.)	$\dot{V}_{E_{BTPS}}$ (L./min.)	$\dot{V}_{E_{STPD}}$ (L./min.)	$F_{E_{O_2}}$ (%)	$F_{E_{CO_2}}$ (%)	RER	$\dot{V}_{O_{2}STPD}$ (L./min.)	$\dot{V}_{O_2}$ (ml./kg./min.)
161.89	175.81	143.27	17.23	3.15	0.839	5.54	73.87

☐ Conduct an exercise and, using an open-circuit method, compute a subject's:

Minute volume (MV)

——————

(L.)

Respiratory quotient (R.Q.)

——————

Oxygen consumption ($\dot{V}_{O_2}$)

——————

(ml./min.)

Oxygen consumption ($\dot{V}_{O_2}$)

——————

(ml./min./kg.)

Oxygen pulse ($\dot{V}_{O_2}$ ml. min./F_H)

——————

Ventilation equivalent for oxygen (VEO₂)

——————

(L./100 ml.)

Rate of oxygen removal ($\dot{V}_{O_2}/\dot{V}$)

——————

(ml./L.)

Oxygen debt

——————

(L.)

☐ Ask subject to hyperventilate for 3 minutes and measure:

Ventilation equivalent for oxygen (VEO₂)

——————

(L./100 ml.)

Rate of oxygen removal ($\dot{V}_{O_2}/\dot{V}$)

——————

(ml./L.)

REFERENCES

Consolazio, C. F., Johnson, R. E., and Pecora, L. J.: Physiological measurements of metabolic functions in man, New York, 1963, McGraw-Hill Book Co.

Dill, D. B., and Fölling, A.: Studies in muscular activity. II. A nomographic description of expired air, J. Physiol. **66**:133, 1928.

Scholander, P.: Analyzer for accurate estimation of respiratory gases in one-half cc samples, J. Biol. Chem. **167**:235, 1947.

SUGGESTED READING

Adams, W.: Influence of age, sex, and body weight on the energy expenditure of bicycle riding, J. Appl. Physiol. **22**:539, 1967.

Dill, D.: Assessment of work performance, J. Sports Med. **6**:3, 1966.

Fowler, K., and Hugh-Jones, P.: Mass-spectrometry applied to clinical practice and research, Brit. Med. J. **1**:1205, 1957.

Kissen, A., and McGuire, D.: New approach for on-line continuous determination of oxygen consumption in human subjects, Aerospace Med. **38**:686, 1967.

Kissen, A., McGuire, D., and Sterling, J.: General description and evaluation of an on-line oxygen uptake computer, Wright-Patterson Air Force Base, Ohio, 1967, Aerospace Medical Research Laboratories.

Magel, J. R., McArdle, W. D., and Glaser, R. M.: Telemetered heart response to selected competitive swimming events, J. Appl. Physiol. **26**:764, 1969.

Margaria, R., Meschia, G., and Marro, F.: Determination of oxygen consumption with Pauling oxygen meter, J. Appl. Physiol. **6**:776, 1954.

Maxfield, M., and Smith, P.: Abbreviated methods for the measurement of oxygen consumption in work physiology, Hum. Factors **9**:587, 1967.

Menn, S., Sinclair, R., and Welch, B.: Effect of inspired Pco_2 up to 30 mm. Hg on response of normal man to exercise, J. Appl. Physiol. **28**:663, 1970.

Shvartz, E.: Energy cost of a handstand, J. Sports Med. **8**:18, 1968.

Stromme, S. B., Kerem, D., and Elsner, R.: Diving bradycardia during rest and exercise and its relation to physical fitness, J. Appl. Physiol. **28**:614, 1970.

Taylor, H., Buskirk, E., and Henschel, A.: Maximal oxygen uptake as an objective measure of cardiorespiratory performance, J. Appl. Physiol. **8**:73, 1955.

Whipp, B. J., and Wasserman, K.: Alveolar-arterial gas tension differences during graded exercise, J. Appl. Physiol. **27**:361, 1969.

Wilmore, J.: Influence of motivation on physical work capacity and performance, J. Appl. Physiol. **24**:459, 1968.

CHAPTER 13

BLOOD LACTATE AND PYRUVATE

THEORY

Morehouse, L. E., and Miller, A. T., Jr.: Physiology of exercise, ed. 6, St. Louis, 1971, The C. V. Mosby Co., chaps. 15, 16, 18.

Åstrand, P-O., and Rodahl, K.: Textbook of work physiology, New York, 1970, McGraw-Hill Book Co., chap. 5.

Differences in lactate and pyruvate are found between blood from arteries and blood from deep and superficial veins, showing that these substances are not uniformly distributed throughout the vascular system. However, values are similar in arterial and fingertip blood when the hand is previously warmed. Correlations of changes of lactate and pyruvate with oxygen supply and tissue circulation are founded on studies of such arterialized blood.

The concentration of lactic acid in a fluid is determined chloridimetrically by the method of Barker and Summerson. Lactic acid is oxidized to acetaldehyde by treating with concentrated sulfuric acid. Acetaldehyde condenses parahydroxy-diphenyl to form a lavender color.

Materials for obtaining fingertip blood sample

- [ ] Interval timer or clock
- [ ] Water bath set at 45° C.
- [ ] Sampling bottles, 50 ml. Erlenmeyer flasks
- [ ] Trichloroacetic acid (TCA)
- [ ] Chemical balance
- [ ] 80% alcohol
- [ ] Sharp blood lancet or scalpel blade for finger puncture
- [ ] Electric centrifuge
- [ ] Serological pipettes, 5 and 10 ml.
- [ ] Glass-stoppered tubes, 15 ml.

Precautions

- [ ] Clean glassware with detergent, not cleaning solution.
- [ ] Protect cleaned glassware from dust and from the lactic acid of the skin. Do not touch the edges of the test tubes and other glassware.
- [ ] Protect all reagents from organic matter.

Procedures, fingertip blood sampling, arterialized capillary blood

- [ ] Warm hand for 5 minutes in water bath at 45° C.
- [ ] Weigh sampling bottle containing 15 ml. of trichloroacetic acid (TCA)
- [ ] Clean the tip of a finger with alcohol. Inflict a wound on fingertip and without constricting the veins allow a few drops of blood to flow directly into the sampling bottle with TCA.

☐ Shake the bottle carefully to disperse drops of blood.

☐ Calculate the weight of blood sampled by comparing the weights of sampling bottles with and without blood.

☐ Transfer sampled blood and TCA to a centrifuge, spin down for 10 minutes at 3000 r.p.m., and draw off the clean supernatant liquid for determination of lactate and pyruvate. Sealed supernatant liquid can be stored for 48 hours.

LACTIC ACID, DETERMINATION AND ANALYSIS
Materials

☐ Metal racks (aluminum) for test tubes

☐ Test tubes with ground glass stoppers, 15 ml.; diameter 2 cm., length 15 cm.

☐ Syringe pipettes, 1, 3, and 5 ml.

☐ Ice bath

☐ Water bath, thermostatically controlled at 30° C.

☐ Water bath, thermostatically controlled at 60° C.

☐ Boiling water bath

☐ Stopwatch

☐ Interval timer

☐ Cuvettes, 19 by 150 mm.

☐ Spectrophotometer

☐ Chemical balance

Reagents

☐ Sulfuric acid (H_2SO_4), concentrated reagent grade, chilled

☐ Lithium lactate, prepared from lithium hydroxide and lactic acid twice recrystallized from solution

☐ Copper sulfate ($CuSO_4$), 20% solution (20 gm. $CuSO_4$/100 ml. H_2O)

☐ Trichloroacetic acid, 10% solution, for deproteinizing blood samples and dilution of working standards of lithium lactate

☐ Parahydroxy-diphenyl, 1.5% solution, dissolved in 2% hydroxide solution that is made fresh weekly

☐ Distilled water, glass distilled

☐ Reagent blanks and two standard solutions with different concentrations of lactic acid

Modified method of Barker and Summerson

☐ Take 1 ml. of the supernatant liquid (blood in TCA) with a volumetric pipette and empty it into a test tube that is kept in an ice bath. To this sample add 5 ml. of concentrated sulfuric acid (H_2SO_4), previously chilled in a refrigerator. The H_2SO_4, too, is added by means of a volumetric pipette, with a cotton wool plug used at the mouthpiece to safeguard against sucking acid into the mouth. The acid is added very slowly, with continuous agitation of the tube, while the tube is held in the ice bath to prevent the solution from getting too hot. The acid being viscous, time for drainage from the pipette is standardized by using a stopwatch.

☐ Two standard solutions of lactic acid are made up, each containing not less than 1 μg. (microgram) and not more than 9 μg. of lactic acid. From each solution 1 ml. is taken, and these standards should receive the same treatment as the samples throughout.

☐ Add to the acid solution in the tube 0.1 ml. or 3 drops of a 20% copper sulfate solution ($CuSO_4$). Shake tube carefully to effect thorough mixing and then place it in a water bath, thermostatically controlled at $60° \pm 0.5°$ C., for 30 minutes.

☐ Take the tube out of the water bath and thoroughly cool it in an ice bath; then add 0.1 ml. of a 1.5% parahydroxy-diphenyl solution. The temperature of the solution in the tube at this stage is critical, and the color-reagent should not be introduced while the contents are still warm. Thoroughly mix the color-reagent, which is insoluble in acid medium, by careful shaking of the tube; then place it in a water bath kept at $30° \pm 0.5°$ C. Incubate the solution at $30°$ C. for 20 minutes. The time of exposure is not critical, provided it is not shorter than 20 minutes and not longer than 50 minutes. All samples, as well as the controls and standards, should receive the same treatment. During the 20-minute period shake the tube occasionally to keep the color-reagent, which is in the form of a suspension, thoroughly mixed.

☐ From the bath at $30°$ C. place the tube into vigorously boiling water for exactly 90 seconds.

☐ Thereafter it is first cooled in ice water for approximately 5 minutes to reach room temperature and is then read in the spectrophotometer at wavelength 360 mμ.

Calculation of blood lactate concentration (LA$_b$)

Lactic acid (mg.)/100 ml. blood =

$$\frac{\text{O.D. of unknown} \times \text{Dilution}}{\text{Aliquot used (ml.)}} \times \frac{100}{1} \times \frac{1}{1000} \quad (22)$$

Example:
Weight of bottle + 15 ml. of TCA = 30.100 gm.
Weight of bottle + 15 ml. of TCA + blood = 30.400 gm.
Weight of blood = 0.3000 gm. = 300 mg.
Percentage of water in blood = 80%; therefore 300 mg. of blood contains 240 mg. of water = 0.24 ml. of water.

Spectrophotometer readings, use in calculation. Division of the mean reagent blank reading by the sample reading or standard solution reading gives the optical density, O.D., or transmittancy of the solution.

☐ 1 ml. of solution TCA + blood = 95.0% transmittancy.

☐ Reagent blank solution = 98.0% transmittancy.

☐ Optical density of the sample is $\frac{98}{95} = 1.037$.

☐ Plot the log of the optical densities of the standard solutions against concentration of lactic acid in micrograms.

☐ Read the log of O.D. = 1.027, off the standard curve, to give the content of the sample in micrograms: the value is 3 mg.

☐ For 0.300 gm. of blood (15 ml. of TCA) the content is 45 mg. Therefore, 45 μg. is dissolved in 0.24 ml. of blood water, and $\frac{1000 \times 45}{0.24}$ will be contained in a liter of blood water. Expressed in terms of milligrams of lactic acid, it becomes then:

$$\frac{1000 \times 45}{1000 \times 0.24} = \frac{45}{0.24} = 187.5 \text{ mg.}$$

and in terms of mg. lactic acid/100 ml. blood it is 18.75 mg.%.

Enzyme method of lactate determination (Scholz et al.)

The enzymatic assay of lactic acid by spectrophotometric determination of diphosphopyridine (DPN) absorption employs the use of a photometer.

Lactate dehydrogenase (LDH) catalyzes the following reaction:

$$\text{L-lactate} + \text{DPN}^+ \rightleftharpoons \text{pyruvate} + \text{DPNH} + \text{H}^+$$
where DPN^+ = diphosphopyridine nucleotide
and DPNH = reduced diphosphopyridine nucleotide

The equilibrium of this reaction is very much in favor of lactate and DPN. It can, however, be displaced completely in favor of pyruvate and DPNH by an excess of DPN, an alkaline medium, and by trapping with hydrozine the pyruvate formed in the above reaction. Under such conditions, lactate is converted quantitatively into pyruvate, with DPN being hydrated in a stoichiometric proportion. The DPNH thus obtained is a measure of the activity.

Materials

- [ ] Bottles
- [ ] Pipettes
- [ ] Centrifuge tubes
- [ ] Plastic spatulas
- [ ] Test tubes
- [ ] Water bath and thermometer
- [ ] Photometer

Reagents

- [ ] 1 N L–lactic acid solution
- [ ] Glycine
- [ ] Hydrazine hydrate
- [ ] Diphosphopyridine nucleotide
- [ ] Lactate dehydrogenase
- [ ] Perchloric acid (reagent grade, density 1.67, 70%; e.g., Merck no. 519)
- [ ] Distilled water

Solutions (sufficient for 25 assays), preparation

1. Glycine buffer: Dilute a solution of 0.5 M glycine and 0.4 M hydrazine, pH 9, in distilled water to 50 ml. Mark bottle "No. 1."
2. DPN solution: Dissolve 0.027 M DPN in 5 ml. of distilled water. Mark bottle "No. 2."
3. LDH suspension: Crystallized suspension of 2 mg. of protein per milliliter, undiluted. Mark bottle "No. 3."
4. Perchloric acid: Dilute 5 ml. of 70% (6.5 ml. of 60%) perchloric acid with distilled water to 100 ml. Mark bottle "No. 4."

Procedures

Deproteinization

- [ ] Pipette successively into a centrifuge tube 1 ml. of perchloric acid (bottle no. 4) and 1 ml. of blood or serum.
- [ ] Mix well with a plastic spatula.
- [ ] Centrifuge for 5 to 10 minutes at 3000 r.p.m.
- [ ] Use 0.1 ml. of the deproteinized supernatant for the assay.

Assay

☐ Prepare a control sample with 1 N L–lactic acid diluted 1:1000 to obtain a solution of 9 µg. L–lactic acid/0.1 ml. For the measurement do not use more than 25 µg. of the lactate control.

☐ Prepare a reagent blank by diluting 1 volume of perchloric acid (bottle no. 4) with 1 volume of distilled water. Use 0.1 ml. of the dilute perchloric acid as the reagent blank.

☐ Pipette accurately into a test tube in the following sequence:

> 2.00 ml. buffer solution (no. 1)
> 0.10 ml. deproteinized supernatant
> 0.03 ml. LDH suspension (no. 3)
> 0.20 ml. DPN solution (no. 2)

☐ Mix well by gentle agitation and allow to stand in a water bath of 25° C., for exactly 1 hour.

☐ Read absorbency at 340 or 366 mµ, against air or a cell filled with water. Deduct the absorbency of the reagent blank from the measuring value to obtain the change in absorbency, ΔA, caused by the lactate:

> At 340 mµ, ΔA × 62.5 = mg.% lactate* in the blood
> ΔA × 67.6 = mg.% lactate* per milliliter in the serum
> At 366 mµ, ΔA × 117.5 = mg.% lactate* in the blood
> ΔA × 127 = mg.% lactate* per milliliter in the serum

PYRUVIC ACID, DETERMINATION AND ANALYSIS (MODIFIED METHOD OF FRIEDMANN ET AL.)
Materials

☐ Spectrophotometer, DU model (Beckman) or models B, BB
☐ Burette, 50 ml.
☐ Pipettes, volumetric and Pasteur, 1, 2, 3, 4, and 5 ml.
☐ Fuming cupboard
☐ Nitrogen (N_2) gas
☐ Test tubes
☐ Accurate chemical balance
☐ Volumetric flasks

Reagents

☐ 10% trichloroacetic acid
☐ *o*-xylene (BP)
☐ 1.0 N sodium carbonate solution (Na_2CO_3): 90 gm. of Na_2CO_3 dissolved in 1 L. of distilled water, previously boiled and cooled
☐ 1.0 N sodium hydroxide (NaOH): 40 gm. of NaOH dissolved in 1 L. of distilled water, previously boiled and thoroughly cooled
☐ 2,4-dinitrophenylhydrazine, 250 mg., dissolved in 100 ml. of RCL (c), diluted to 500 ml. with distilled water

Solutions

☐ Standard pyruvic acid solution is prepared from weighed quantities of freshly vacuum-redistilled pyruvic acid. Commercial sodium pyruvate is standardized

---

*Calculated as free acid (not lactate ions).

against the redistilled pure acid. The sodium pyruvate must be thoroughly de-hydrated in an oven at 80° C. before use. Standard solutions are made up daily so that 3 ml. quantities contain, respectively, 5, 10, and 15 μg. of pyruvic acid.

Analysis

☐ From the same supernatant liquid used for lactate estimations take 3.0 ml. with a volumetric pipette and introduce it into a wide-mouth tube.

☐ To the 3 ml. sample add 2 ml. of 2,4-dinitrophenylhydrazine solution with thorough mixing.

☐ Leave the mixture for 5 minutes at room temperature and then add 4 ml. of o-xylene.

☐ Aerate the solution in the tube with nitrogen gas for 1 minute (pressure 3 p.s.i.).

☐ Extract and discard the trichloroacetic acid with a Pasteur pipette.

☐ To the remaining solution in the tube add 5.0 ml. of sodium carbonate solution and repeat the aeration for 1 minute.

☐ Extract the sodium carbonate solution quantitatively and collect it in another tube.

☐ Add further 2 ml. of sodium carbonate solution to the original tube and again aerate.

☐ Extract this solution of Na_2CO_3 and add it to the first extracted Na_2CO_3; take a 4.0 ml. sample and alkalinize it with 1 ml. of 1.0 N NaOH.

☐ Centrifuge the solution to have a clear solution for reading in the spectrophotom-eter at wavelength 520.

Calculation of pyruvic acid concentration

Division of the mean blank reading by the sample or standard reading gives the optical density (transmittancy).

Example:

Blank reading = 98.0% transmittancy
Sample reading = 95.0% transmittancy

$$\text{Sample O.D.} = \frac{98}{95} = 1.027$$

Percentage water in blood = 80%
Weight of blood samples = 300 mg.
Sample of TCA taken for analysis (whole sample is 15 ml.) = 3 ml.
O.D. of sample = 1.027

☐ Plot the log of the optical densities of the three standard solutions against con-centration of pyruvic acid. From this standard curve, the concentration of pyruvic acid (read off for the log of an O.D. of 1.027) = 5 μg. The 5 μg. is contained in the 3 ml. of TCA; therefore, the whole sample of 15 ml. contains:

$$\frac{15}{3} \times \frac{5}{1} = 25 \ \mu\text{g. pyruvic acid}$$

This means that 300 mg. of blood (0.24 ml. blood water; 80% water in blood) contains 25 μg. of pyruvic acid.

☐ Calculate the quantity for a liter of blood water as follows:

$$\frac{1000 \times 25}{0.24} \ \text{micrograms or} \ \frac{1000 \times 25 \ \text{milligrams}}{0.24 \times 1000} = \frac{25}{0.24} \ \text{milligrams per liter blood water}$$

In terms of mg. pyruvic acid/100 ml. blood it is 10.42 mg.%.

TOTAL BODY LACTATE

Total body lactate is calculated from the following formula:

$$LA_{kg.} = \frac{0.61}{0.80} \; LA_b \tag{23}$$

where: $LA_{kg.}$ = total body lactate in grams per kilogram body weight
0.61 = fraction of body water
0.80 = fraction of blood water
LA_b = blood lactate in grams per liter of blood

Proficiency check

Task	Date completed	Instructor's initials
1. Obtain fingertip blood sample.	_____	_____
2. Perform lactic acid determination.	_____	_____
3. Perform pyruvic acid determination.	_____	_____
4. Estimate total body lactate.	_____	_____

REFERENCES

Barker, S., and Summerson, W.: The chlorimetric determination of lactic acid in biological material, J. Biol. Chem. **138**:535, 1941.

Friedmann, T., Haugen, G., and Kmieciak, T.: The level of pyruvic and lactic acids and the lactic-pyruvate ratio in the blood of human subjects, J. Biol. Chem. **157**:673, 1945.

Scholz, R., Schmitz, H., Bücher, T., and Lampen J. O.: Über die Wirkung von Nystatin auf Bäckerhefe, Biochem. Z. **331**:71, 1959.

SUGGESTED READING

Consolazio, C. F., Johnson, R. E., and Pecora, L. J.: Physiological measurements of metabolic functions in man, New York, 1963, McGraw-Hill Book Co.

Huckabee, W.: Control of concentration gradients of pyruvate and lactate across cell membranes in blood, J. Appl. Physiol. **9**:163, 1956.

Hullin, R., and Noble, R.: The determination of lactic acid in micro quantities, Biochem. J. **55**:289, 1953.

Margaria, R.: Aerobic and anaerobic energy sources in muscular exercise. In Margaria, R., editor: Exercise at altitude, New York, 1967, Excerpta Medica Foundation.

Margaria, R., et al.: Kinetics and mechanism of oxygen debt contraction in man, J. Appl. Physiol. **18**:371, 1963.

Mohme-Lundholm, E., Svedmyr, E., and Vamos, N.: Enzymatic micromethod for determining the lactic acid content of fingertip blood, Scand. J. Clin. Lab. Invest. **17**:501, 1965.

Rowell, L. B., et al.: Human metabolic responses to hyperthermia during mild to maximal exercise, J. Appl. Physiol. **26**:395, 1969.

Ström, G.: The influence of anoxia on lactate utilization in man after prolonged muscular work, Acta Physiol. Scand. **17**:440, 1949.

CHAPTER 14

ERGOMETRY

THEORY

Morehouse, L. E., and Miller, A. T., Jr.: Physiology of exercise, ed. 6, St. Louis, 1971, The C. V. Mosby Co., chaps. 11, 13, 18.

Åstrand, P-O., and Rodahl, K.: Textbook of work physiology, New York, 1970, McGraw-Hill Book Co., chap. 11, Appendix.

An ergometer (ergo = work, meter = measure) is an instrument in which the amounts of mechanical work per unit of time are registered. The apparatus enables subjects to perform prescribed amounts of work while physiological phenomena accompanying these performances can be measured with stationary instruments. Many ways of performing work are conceivable, but those most frequently used in physiological experiments and functional tests are hand cranking or leg pedaling a bicycle ergometer, walking and running on a treadmill, and bench stepping. Treadmill and step tests are technically nonergometric, since the mechanical work done in walking, running, and stepping is not measured accurately. In treadmill exercise, running on a grade is not running uphill because the mass of the body is not raised. Running uphill requires more energy than running on an equivalent grade on a treadmill. The vertical oscillations of the body during walking and running on a treadmill or stepping up and down on a bench represent positive mechanical work as the body is lifted and negative mechanical work as it is lowered. Bench stepping and cycling also involve substantial unmeasured work, and the efficiency of the work (Chapter 16) varies with the experience of the subject (learning), body weight, and speed of stepping or pedaling.

A summary of evaluations of work-loading devices appears in Table 6. Since the various criteria are not equally weighted and some are more important than others in various situations, it is not possible to score the relative merit of each device.

Ergometers are usually combined with cardiographic (Chapters 7 and 8), spirographic (Chapters 10, 11, and 12), and blood chemistry (Chapter 13) instruments to evaluate physiological responses to continuous effort and to test cardiorespiratory endurance. The stationary instruments used to measure physiological phenomena are attached to the subject by means of hoses and wires, which require the subject to exercise on the same spot and minimize his head and arm movement for respiratory procedures and blood taking. This is one reason why the bicycle ergometer is preferred to the treadmill or stepping bench. More importantly the bicycle ergometer provides the expression of work in watts or kilogram-meters (kg.-m.) per second (1 kg.-m./sec. = about 10 watts). Physiological measures during ergometer pedaling and bench stepping show slightly less variability than responses to treadmill exercise. Using the bicycle ergometer the subject adopts the same position before, during, and after exercise—either sitting or lying. The bicycle ergometer is less alarming for subjects than is the treadmill and gives a greater sense of security.

Table 6. Ranking of laboratory work-loading devices*

Criterion	Type of device		
	Bicycle	Treadmill	Step
Skill and agility required; learning and training in effect; usefulness for high work loads	2	1	3
History of use, data available	2	1	3
Expense: cost, wear, maintenance	2	3	1
Automatic controls available	1	2	3
Ease of physiological measurements	1	2	3
Space required, compactness, weight	2	3	1
Measurement of external work: readout of load, simplicity of calculation	1	3	2
Danger to awkward, older subjects	1	3	2
Ease of calibration	2	3	1
Control of load by heart rate	1	2	3
Flexibility for numerous types of use	1	3	2
Freedom from noise	1	3	2

*1 = most desirable; 2 = intermediate; 3 = least desirable.

Trained young men tolerate higher levels of stress on a treadmill, about 5 to 10% less on a bicycle ergometer, and about 20 to 30% less on a stepping bench. For some reason higher $\dot{V}_{O_{2max}}$ determinations are obtained on a treadmill than on a bicycle ergometer or stepping bench.

It is not possible to establish an exact equivalency of physiological responses to exercise on various types of laboratory work devices when the work load is used as the basis for comparison. Neither can performance on an ergometer be used to predict performance of a work task, such as shoveling sand. This limitation is probably a result of the specificity of physiological responses to different exercises, but it could be due to the use of uncalibrated ergometers. The work loads obtained from such ergometers can be as much as 20% in error. All ergometers need to be calibrated at least twice a year.

Whatever device is used it should be kept in mind that the application of exercise is extremely critical, as the physiological response is entirely dependent upon it. The following factors must be controlled:

☐ Rate of onset of exercise and adjustment of time-load gradation from initial load to test load
☐ Test load level
☐ Duration of test load
☐ Rate of stopping exercise

DEFINITIONS AND FORMULAS

Work (W) The product of force, F, acting against mass through distance, s. Thus:

$$W = Fs \tag{24}$$

Kilopon-meter (kpm) Work in which the product of force, F, acts against a 1000-gram *mass* through a distance, s, measured in meters.

Kilogram-meter (kg.-m.) Work in which the product of force, F, acts against a 1000-gram *weight* through a distance, s, measured in meters.

Work rate (kg.-m./min.) The product of force and distance, Fs, in kilogram-meters or kilopon-meters divided by the unit time, t, in minutes:

$$\frac{\text{Work rate} = \text{Fs} \ (\text{kg.-m.})}{\text{t (min.)}} \tag{25}$$

Watt Work at the rate of 6.1 kilogram-meters per minute (or 1 joule per second, 0.7376 foot-pound per second, or about ¼ calorie per second).

Energy The capacity for overcoming tension.

$$\text{Potential energy} = \text{mgh or wh} \tag{26}$$
$$\text{Kinetic energy} = \tfrac{1}{2} \text{mv}^2 \text{ or wv}^2/2 \text{ g} \tag{27}$$

where: m = mass
g = acceleration of gravity
h = vertical distance
w = weight
v = velocity

BICYCLE ERGOMETERS

In comparison with other laboratory work-loading devices the bicycle ergometer requires the most nearly identical energy expenditures for given settings of work intensity irrespective of sex, age, or body size.

For a given work load the physiological effort is a function of the radius of the crank. The optimum radius of the crank (pedal shaft) for a work load range of 30 to 200 watts is 17 to 18 cm. (about 7 inches).

The force exerted on the axle is not constant during pedaling because of the phasic surges of power during downstrokes. These surges would cause cyclic variations in speed were it not for the weighted flywheel used in ergometers. The standard flywheel is a cylinder of 100 kg. of steel with a radius of 33.3 cm. Due to its moment of inertia a certain amount of energy is required to accelerate the mass to a given angular velocity. In one type (Lanooy) the flywheel energy is approximately 600 joules at 60 r.p.m., requiring a work rate of 200 watts for 3 seconds just to overcome inertia.

Ergometers can be operated from three positions: hand drive while standing (hand cranking), bicycle drive while sitting (upright), and bicycle drive while reclining (supine).

Upright bicycle ergometers have an adjustable seat or saddle. If the seat is too low, the leg muscles will fatigue early. For optimum pedaling efficiency the height of the seat is adjusted individually to allow for an almost completely extended leg at the lowest pedal position. With the front part of the foot on the pedal and the leg extended with the knee only slightly bent, the seat height is proper if the heel is an inch below the front part of the foot. Markings on the seat post are for the purpose of recording on the data sheet the subject's seat height adjustment.

The pedaling frequency is 60 revolutions per minute in light and moderate work and up to 70 in heavy work.

In reporting ergometric data, state room temperature and humidity, body position, and time of day. If metabolic data are included, state the composition of inspired gas.

Express rate of work in watts or in kilogram-meters per minute.

Adjustment procedure

☐ Adjust seat height.
☐ Adjust the pedaling unit so that the pedal axle is approximately 10 inches ahead of the seat post.
☐ Adjust the handlebars to comfortable vertical and fore-and-aft positions. Use

Fig. 14-1. Mechanical bicycle ergometer in use. (Dudley, Hardin, and Yang photograph.)

conventional rather than racing handlebars. (The purpose of underslung racing handlebars is to enable the cyclist to assume a more streamlined position when pedaling against the wind.)

☐ Post the ergometer adjustments on the subject's data sheet.

Mechanical bicycle ergometer (von Döbeln)*

Resistance to pedaling (or hand cranking, described later) is afforded by a friction of a brake belt sliding on a flywheel rim (Fig. 14-1). The frictional resistance is varied and measured by a weighted pendulum attached to the belt. The difference in force at the belt ends is measured by the deflection of the pendulum and read on a scale calibrated in kilograms. This difference in force, or torque, is directly proportional to the load, or braking resistance, F. Adjustment in load is accomplished by a hand wheel that tightens or loosens the brake belt and changes the position of the pendulum in relation to the scale. The turn of the adjustment wheel is highly critical.

*The von Döbeln friction bicycle ergometer is manufactured by the Monark-Crescent AB, Varberg, Sweden.

This system does not take into account the frictional resistance of the chain drive, which may make the total actual load as much as 20% higher than the brake belt load measured on the pendulum scale. This error is greater at lower work loads.

It should be possible to build an ergometer in which the work load is read directly from the pressure of the feet against the pedals.

Pedal revolutions are counted. To maintain a constant work load the subject is required to pedal at a constant rate. The following of a metronome helps, but errors of 10% are easily introduced if a revolution totalizer is not fitted to the ergometer.

The rate of external work, W, is calculated from the braking resistance, F, applied through the distance, s, traveled by the flywheel rim. Relationships are shown in Formula 24 ($W = Fs$):

where W = rate of work in kilogram-meters per minute (kg.-m./min.)
     F = braking resistance in kilograms
     s = distance in meters traveled by the flywheel rim

Example:

$$W = \text{(resistance)} \times \text{(distance traveled by flywheel rim per pedal revolution} \times \text{pedal revolutions per minute)}$$
$$= (2 \text{ kg.}) \times (6 \text{ m.} \times 60)$$
$$= (2 \text{ kg.}) \times (360 \text{ m.})$$
$$= 720 \text{ kg.-m./min.}$$

Calibration

The friction, or mechanical ergometer needs to be calibrated because of the highly variable frictional resistance of the chain drive and the slightly variable frictional resistance of the belt and pendulum system. The latter is checked by hanging a certified weight on the belt and checking the reading on the pendulum scale.

To check the entire system, including the chain drive, use a direct method of calibration using a precision mechanical dynamometer. Apply the calibrating force as close as possible to the point where the subject exerts his force. When a rotating dynamometer is used, its shaft is connected to the axis of the pedal arm of the bicycle ergometer.

Equipment

☐ Friction ergometer, von Döbeln (Monark)
☐ Pedal revolution totalizer
☐ Metronome
☐ Interval timer, clock or stopwatch

Procedure (von Döbeln)

☐ Set the metronome tempo at 120 single beats per minute to control the pedaling rate at 60 revolutions per minute.
☐ Adjust the height of the seat and handlebar.
☐ Seat subject on ergometer without touching the pedals.
☐ Set the mark on the pendulum weight at "0" on the scale.
☐ Simultaneously begin the work, set the desired load, and start the timer.
☐ At the end of the preset work period stop pedaling.

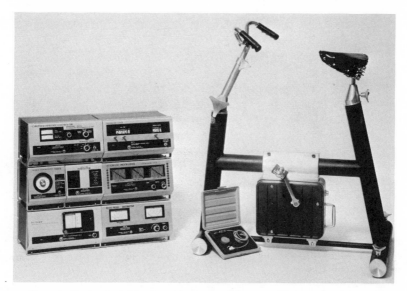

Fig. 14-2. Electrically braked bicycle ergometer. (Courtesy Warren E. Collins, Inc., Braintree, Mass.)

Electric bicycle ergometer

Measurable resistance to pedaling in electric ergometers (Fig. 14-2) is provided by an electromagnetic braking force produced by a direct current generator activated from an outside electrical source. It could be activated from an electrical current produced from an ergometer-driven generator.

The electrical output in watts is converted into mechanical work units, kilogram-meters (kg.-m.), following the formula:

$$1 \text{ watt} = 6.1 \text{ kg.-m./min.}$$

Electrically braked bicycle ergometer

It is not necessary to control the frequency of pedaling at an exact rate when using an electric ergometer. Increases in pedal revolutions are in effect increases in current permitted through the brake, thus decreasing the resistance. Likewise decreases in pedal revolutions result in a decreased current flow and increased resistance. At slower pedal speeds the brake resistance is higher, tending to tire the leg muscles. At higher speeds, 60 r.p.m. and above, local fatigue of leg musculature is avoided and the stress is more of a cardiopulmonary nature. The physiological effort at low revolutions is greater than at higher revolutions, especially at heavier work loads (above 200 watts). Most bicycle ergometer tests are standardized at 50 or 60 r.p.m.; the 60 r.p.m. speed is preferable.

Linearity of output, in watts, is governed by circuit design. The range over which this compensation is effective is from 35 to 75 r.p.m.

AUTOMATIC HEART RATE CONTROL (MOREHOUSE-COLLINS CARDIOTACHIMETRIC CONTROLLER)

An electronic controller containing a comparison amplifier that combines feedback from heart rate and heart rate acceleration (Fig. 14-3) automatically adjusts

Fig. 14-3. Morehouse-Collins automatic heart rate controller. (Courtesy Warren E. Collins, Inc., Braintree, Mass.)

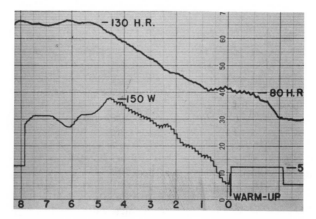

Fig. 14-4. Sample recorder tracing from the Morehouse-Collins system. Read from right to left.

the intensity of exercise (regulates the brake load application) to achieve the desired heart rate. Acceleration of the heart rate is controlled at a preset speed change. The maximum rate of load application is preset at 60 watts per minute per minute. Step changes in brake load occur every 7 seconds and do not exceed 10 watts—a smooth transition. The greatest increase in heart rate permitted by the circuit is 15 beats in 1 minute. If the subject's heart rate change is excessive, the rate of load application is diminished. This feature enables an investigator to exercise a subject at any heart rate desired. The subject pedals at approximately 60 r.p.m., and the ergometer loading is regulated by the subject's heart rate according to a predetermined program. No adjustments by the subject or the examiner are required. The examiner is free to give full attention to the responses of the exercising subject.

An emergency turnoff on the cardiotachimetric controller is set at 10 beats above the subject's maximum desired heart rate. If this preset rate is exceeded, the controller instantly reduces the ergometer work load to zero and turns on the trip off light. If the trip off light is on, raising the reset lever applies a 50-watt load on the ergometer and disengages the emergency cutoff.

Calibration

Calibrate and adjust automated systems in accordance with the performance requirements set forth below.

Standards of acceptability for automated ergometric systems

Ergometer accuracy (watts)

Calibrator	Instrument
50	42- 58
100	92-108
150	142-158
200	192-208
250	242-258

Ergometer repeatability (monthly recalibration)
Within scale of plus or minus 3 watts from 50 to 250 watts.
Pedal speed meter
Within plus or minus 3 r.p.m. at all true speeds between 50 and 70 r.p.m.
Cardiotachimetric controller
Controls heart rate at a preset level within plus or minus 4 beats per minute at all pulse-generated steady heart rates between 120 and 180 per minute.

True heart rate readout on panel meter can be adjusted to match pulse generator within plus or minus 2 beats per minute at 90, 120, 150, and 180 per minute and will not drift more than 2 beats per minute during continuous operation for 1 hour.

Rate of rise of load application is between 55 and 65 watts per minute per minute.

Programmer
Program heart rate and watts must correspond with meter readouts on the controller and ergometer panels.
Integrator
Total work reading within plus or minus 3 units when dynamometer-operated ergometer is driven at work rates of 25, 100, and 300 watts each for 3 periods of 1 minute.
Recorder (readout range from 40 to 200 beats per minute)
Heart rate and watt readouts can be adjusted to true heart rate and to work rate at heart rates of 50, 100, 150, and 200, and at work rates of 25, 50, 75, 100, 150, and 200 watts.

Heart rate—controlled ergometric operating procedure (Morehouse-Collins)

☐ Arrange units on a table, left of the bicycle ergometer and facing forward. Programmer—lower left. Recorder—lower right. Ergometer control—upper left. Cardiotachimetric controller—center right. Integrator—upper right.

☐ Wire as coded.

☐ Set unit PE switch down.

☐ Power on.

☐ Calibrate and adjust.

☐ Set emergency turnoff at safe upper limit of heart rate for subject.

☐ Set cardiotachometric controller selector to "automatic program."

☐ Set programmer selector to "program heart rate."

☐ Set programmer "minutes per step."

☐ Set programmer "heart rate per step."

☐ Set programmer "watts per step" if any part of the program is on "program work rate."

☐ Set programmer start and step to "program complete."

☐ Set total work integrator to "0."

☐ Adjust seat height.

☐ Attach earpiece.

☐ Start recorder.

☐ Start program.

☐ Fan on.

☐ When step no. 2 light goes on, start pedaling. Instruct the subject to "commence pedaling and hold the speed fairly constant at 60 r.p.m. during the entire exercise period." Warning lights on the ergometer control and on the remote pedal tachometer will blink if the pedal speed falls below 35 r.p.m., the lower limit of the circuit's compensation.

☐ Ten seconds after increase speed light goes out, press reset switch upward.

☐ Read work totals from integrator at end of each step, and at end of exercise if terminated early.

☐ At the end of the preset work period stop pedaling.

☐ At the termination of exercise if a "tapering off" exercise is to be performed, set the manual trip to "low load" (50 watts). At the end of this period (e.g., 2 minutes) stop pedaling.

☐ At the end of the recovery period (e.g., 5 minutes) shut the recorder off.

☐ Power off.

Fig. 14-5. Motor-driven treadmill. (Courtesy W. E. Quinton, Seattle, Wash.)

☐ From recorder obtain work rate and heart rate chart.

☐ From integrator obtain total work.

☐ Reset integrator to zero.

TREADMILL

Certain features of design should be incorporated in the treadmill (Fig. 14-5) for exercise physiology studies. These are listed below.

1. Belt speed can be quickly and reliably adjustable by remote control from a range of 2 to 20 m.p.h.
2. Belt is wide enough to permit reasonable amount of lateral change of position by the subject.
3. Belt is long enough to accommodate the longer stride of tall subjects.
4. Grade is quickly and reliably adjustable by remote control from 0% (level) to 30%.
5. The platforms on either side of the belt should have a low profile so that the subject can move with ease onto and from the belt.

The variables that can be measured in treadmill exercise are the speed of the treadmill, angle of inclination, body weight, length of each step, and step frequency. These are measurements that are not easily expressed in exact physical units.

The motor-driven treadmill does not record the external physical work of a subject walking or running on it. Instead the work is estimated by calculating the product of body mass times the "vertical distance." When the treadmill bed is flat and the subject walks on the level surface, the vertical distance being traversed is zero. Therefore, the product of body mass times vertical distance is zero, so no physical work is accomplished.*

When a treadmill grade, or incline, is established, physical work during walking and running on it is estimated by measuring the body mass (weighing the subject) and expressing the vertical distance as a grade percentage, reflecting the units of rise or vertical displacement per hundred horizontal units of distance traveled. For example, a +5% grade is interpreted as a 5-meter vertical displacement for every 100 meters of belt movement. Use the following physical formula:

$$W = Fs$$

where W = rate of work in kilogram-meters per minute (kg.-m./min.)

F = subject's body weight in kilograms ($Wt._{kg.}$)

s = total revolutions in 1 minute (r.p.m.) times belt length in meters times grade %/100

In converting the degree of slope of a treadmill to grade, in engineering terms the grade is defined as the tangent of the angle theta. Table 7 facilitates conversion of treadmill elevation from degrees to percent.

The treadmill motor can be reversed, or the bed angled to provide for downhill walking and running.

Treadmill procedure

☐ Ascertain that no one is standing on the treadmill.

☐ Start the treadmill.

---

*The external work of level walking and running can be approximated by the formula of Coates and Meade: $L = (P - d)^2 \times W/(8R)$, where L = the lift work per step in kilogram-meters, P = pace length in meters, d = foot length in meters, W = body weight in kilograms, and R = leg length in meters.

SAMPLE DATA SHEET

Subject ID	Condition	F (Body weight) (kg.)	Belt revolutions (r.p.m.)	Belt length (m.)	Grade (%)	s	Rate of work (kg.-m./min.)
Example	good	75	14.0	6.0	+5.0	4.2	315.0

☐ Adjust speed.
☐ Adjust grade.
☐ Give instructions to subject, as follows:
  1. Stand on left side platform facing forward (belt running toward subject).
  2. Grasp forward handrail with right hand, then with right foot step forward on center of belt, and start walking.
  3. After gaining balance and proper (upright, not slumped) posture, let go of handrail. Maintain position on forward portion of belt.
  4. To step off the treadmill, grasp the handrail and step onto the platform with the left foot.

Prediction of $\dot{V}_{O_{2max}}$ from treadmill performance (Balke formula)

Procedure

☐ Subject is to walk (or run) on a motor-driven treadmill at a speed of 90 meters per minute (3.4 m.p.h.). Arms swing freely, not grasping a support.
☐ Grade is increased from horizontal, one degree at the end of the first minute, and one degree thereafter until the subject's limit is reached.
☐ From the ultimate grade calculate $\dot{V}_{O_2}$ from the following Balke formula:

$$\dot{V}_{O_{2max}} \text{ (ml./min./kg.)}_{STPD} = \text{Speed (m./min.)} \times (0.073 + \text{grade \%}/100) \times (1.8) \quad (28)$$

Example

$$\dot{V}_{O_{2max}} = (90) \times \left(0.073 + \frac{23.5}{100}\right) \times (1.8) = 50 \text{ ml./min./kg.}_{STPD}$$

Notes

☐ Do not correct for pressure (altitude) or temperature. The derivation of Balke's formula takes these into account.
☐ In registering treadmill grade, Balke's equation uses the sine of the angle theta instead of the engineering definition, which uses the tangent of theta. However, in the grades reached in this test the sine and the tangent are not much different, so either may be used.
☐ The values for $\dot{V}_{O_{2max}}$ from the Balke formula may be too high because the sub-

Table 7. Treadmill elevation conversion

Degrees	Percent	Degrees	Percent
0.567	1	8.534	15
1	1.75	9	15.84
1.150	2	9.083	16
1.716	3	9.650	17
2	3.49	10	17.63
2.300	4	10.200	18
2.850	5	10.750	19
3	5.24	11	19.44
3.434	6	11.300	20
4	7	11.852	21
4.567	8	12	21.26
5	8.75	12.400	22
5.150	9	12.950	23
5.716	10	13.484	24
6	10.51	14	24.93
6.267	11	14.033	25
6.834	12	14.567	26
7	12.29	15	26.79
7.400	13	15.100	27
7.967	14		

ject may continue work beyond his $\dot{V}_{O_{2max}}$. They will be too low if the subject quits well before his limit is reached.

STEPPING BENCH

Both positive and negative work is accomplished during performance of a stepping exercise. The climbing phase is positive work because the ascent is achieved in opposition to the gravitational force and the body mass must be lifted each step. The descent stage is negative work due to the assist from the gravitational force as the body mass is lowered. The mechanical work of descending has not been determined. It is estimated to be from $\frac{1}{3}$ to $\frac{1}{7}$ the work of stepping up. The energy expenditure of descending from a step is estimated to be from 25% ($\frac{1}{4}$) to 33$\frac{1}{3}$% ($\frac{1}{3}$) that of ascending. The value depends on the ease (efficiency) of stepping.

Holding to any fixed object during the stepping exercise must be avoided, as it alters the motions of stepping and affects the effort.

Intermediate rates of stepping, 20 to 30 ascents per minute, are the most comfortable, the most efficient, and yield the most consistent data. Low rates of ascent, 15 or fewer ascents, per minute, are more difficult than intermediate rates because the movement is discontinuous. High rates, 40 or more ascents per minute, lead to tripping and require concentration and learning. When a high bench is used (18 to 20 inches), a stepping rate of 20 ascents per minute is optimal. The rate of stepping has more influence on efficiency than the bench height.

The height of the stepping bench may be either fixed or variable. The variable-height bench can be set to the nearest centimeter between 10 and 50 cm. If it is not infinitely adjustable, employing a screw and crank or a hydraulic lift, it is advantageous to provide benches with step heights of 10, 20, 30, 40, and 50 cm. (or their English approximations of 4, 8, 12, 16, and 20 inches). To obtain progressively increasing work loads during continuous exercise it must be possible to change the stepping height rapidly while maintaining a constant rate of stepping.

The intensity of the stepping exercise can be varied either by adjusting the height of the bench (when using a variable-height bench) or by adjusting the stepping rate (when using a fixed bench).

In order to obtain maximum oxygen consumption values in fit young subjects, steps whose total height is 40 to 50 cm. and stepping rates above 30 ascents per minute are required. As this arrangement requires high agility, the stepping bench is rarely used for direct measurement of maximum oxygen consumption or maximum work capacity. The stepping bench is commonly used for submaximal tests, from which estimates can be made of the subject's maximum performance.

Since body weight is a significant factor in bench stepping, it is necessary in studies comparing individuals to correct for differences in body weight. This is done by adjusting the bench height or the stepping rate according to the procedures that follow.

Adjustment of step height to body weight

Desired work rate is obtained by adjusting the height of the bench to body weight in accordance with Formula 29.*

$$\text{Step height (cm.)} = \frac{\text{Work rate (kg.-cm./min.)}}{\text{Step rate (per minute)} \times \text{body weight (kg.)}} \tag{29}$$

Example

$$x = \frac{45{,}000}{20 \times 75} = 30 \text{ cm.}$$

Adjustment of stepping rate to body weight

Desired work rate is obtained by adjusting the stepping rate to body weight in accordance with Formula 30.*

$$\text{Stepping rate (steps/min.)} = \frac{\text{Work load (kg.-cm./min.)}}{\text{Bench height (cm.)} \times \text{body weight (kg.)}} \tag{30}$$

Example

$$x = \frac{45{,}000}{30 \times 75} = 20 \text{ steps per minute}$$

Stepping instructions

☐ Face the step at the signal "up" place the left foot on the bench.

☐ At signal "two" step all the way up and place the right foot on the bench, straightening both legs, body upright, back straight. Stand up fully so you can remain standing there if required to do so. No crouching, bouncing off the edge of the step in a stiff-legged manner, or pushing up the body by hands on thighs. Arm swinging is permitted. Touch the marker with the head (if a sensor is used).

☐ At signal "three" immediately and in rhythm step back down again with the left foot.

☐ At signal "four" return the right foot to the floor.

---

*This formula does not take into account the work of descending.

☐ Continue in a marching count: "up-two, three, four."

Taping these instructions for playback during testing assures the standardization of procedures. During mass testing, error in identification is avoided if each subject is issued a disk with a number on it that is worn on a necklace. The number is written in chalk on the bench.

Equipment

☐ Stepping benches the following heights: 10, 20, 30, 40, and 50 cm. (Or 4, 8, 12, 16, and 20 inches)

☐ Two-step benches, Masters or Roth

☐ Metronome

☐ Stopwatch

☐ Stethoscope and rubber strap

☐ Chair

☐ Scales, accurate to 0.5 kg., and certified weights for calibration

☐ Oral thermometer

☐ Physiological monitoring equipment: ECG, blood pressure, and oxygen consumption measuring equipment

☐ ID necklace

☐ Data sheets

Stepping ergometer test (Balke)

A series of benches of 10, 20, 30, and 40 cm. heights are placed next to each other so that the subject can change the stepping height rapidly. The stepping rate is 30 ascents per minute. After each 3 minute period the stepping height is increased 10 cm. without any interruption of the stepping rate. In order to avoid muscular fatigue the leading foot is altered periodically. Unless monitoring procedures indicate that the test should be terminated earlier (Chapter 2), the subject proceeds from the 10 cm. bench to the 20 cm. bench and so on after each 3-minute period of stepping, until the heart rate reaches 160 beats per minute or until the exercise on the 40 cm. bench is completed. The heart rate is taken during the third minute of exercise at each level and recorded on a chart. The points are connected by lines and a curve thus formed is extended by extrapolation to a "critical" heart rate, such as 85% of maximum depending on the subject's age (Table 4). Projection of the intersecting point of the curve and the "critical" heart rate level vertically to the baseline, which is calibrated to indicate oxygen requirements for various work loads according to the following Balke formula:

$$\dot{V}_{O_2} = (f \times h \times 1.33 \times 1.78) + 10.5 \qquad (31)$$

where $\dot{V}_{O_2}$ = oxygen requirement (in ml./kg./min.)

f = stepping rate, or ascents per minute

h = height of the step in meters (1 cm. = 0.01 m.)

1.33 = work involved in the ascent + one third for the descent

1.78 = ml. of oxygen required for 1 kg.-m. of work

10.5 = 10.5 ml./kg./min. oxygen requirement for the forward and backward stepping in addition to the vertical movement

Procedure (subject)

☐ Rest in a chair for 15 minutes while ECG, blood pressure, heart rate, and respiratory gas exchange apparatus are applied. Record is made of resting metabolic rate.

☐ Exercise on the 10 cm. bench at 30 steps per minute for 3 minutes as introduction to the equipment and work procedure.

☐ Rest in the chair for 3 minutes.

☐ Exercise on the 10 cm. bench at 30 steps per minute for 3 minutes.

☐ Exercise on the 20 cm. bench at 30 steps per minute for 3 minutes.

☐ Exercise on the 30 cm. bench at 30 steps per minute for 3 minutes.

☐ Exercise on the 40 cm. bench at 30 steps per minute for 3 minutes.

☐ Continue to step in place on the floor for 3 minutes to prevent pooling of blood in lower extremities.

☐ Rest in the chair for 3 minutes or until all symptoms of distress have disappeared.

Procedure (examiner)

☐ Prepare to record the heart rate during the third minute of exercise at each level and prepare to terminate the test at a 160 heart rate or at the first sign of approaching limits of capacity (review Chapter 2).

☐ Calculate $\dot{V}_{O_2}$ at the "critical" heart rate, using Formula 31.

Harvard step test—rapid form (Weiss and Phillips)

Rating of physical fitness for hard work and evaluating effects of training can be achieved by measuring the recovery heart rate following a standard exercise. The Harvard step test is commonly employed for healthy young men. No adjustment for body weight is made. A cadence of 30 steps per minute is fixed for all. Sloan has modified the test for females by using a 17-inch step rather than the 20-inch height prescribed by Brouha et al.

This test is not a reliable predictor of muscular strength or endurance and does not correlate highly with other "fitness" tests.

The original test calls for three postexercise heart rate determinations, whereas only one is needed because of the high intercorrelation of the various postexercise heart rates. Thus a rapid form, utilizing one postexercise count, is adequate.

Procedure

INSTRUCTIONS. "Step onto and down from the bench 30 times per minute for 5 minutes or until compelled by fatigue to stop. Immediately after the exercise sit down. The pulse will be counted from 1 to 1½ minutes after exercise."

ADMINISTRATION

☐ Play taped instructions and demonstrate stepping technique.

☐ Set metronome at 120 per minute.

☐ Give practice in 4-count stepping exercise:

"Up"	Left foot up
"Two"	Right foot up; stand erect
"Three"	Left foot down
"Four"	Right foot down

☐ When ready, start stopwatch and have subject start stepping.

☐ After 5 minutes of stepping, or when subject is compelled by fatigue to stop, record time on stopwatch in seconds on data sheet and instruct subject to sit down.

☐ Shut off metronome.

☐ Take the pulse rate for 30 seconds during the interval from 1 to 1½ minutes after exercise.

☐ Calculate Fitness Index (FI) from the following formula:

$$FI = \frac{\text{Duration of exercise in seconds} \times 100}{5.5 \times \text{Pulse count } 1\text{-}1\frac{1}{2} \text{ min. after exercise}}$$ (32)

Classifications: above 80, very good
60 to 80, good
40 to 60, average
Below 40, poor

SAMPLE DATA SHEET

Name	Sex	Bench height (cm.)	Duration of exercise (sec.)	Pulse at 1-1½ min. (bpm)	FI score	Classification
Example	M	40	300	78	70	Good

Two-step benches

Two-step elevations require the work of both legs and thus avoid overtiring of one leg as with single-step benches.

A 1.33 factor (⅓ of work of stepping up) is assumed for stepping down work. For a step bench with two 1-foot steps the formula for computing physical work would be as follows:

Work (ft.-lb./min.) = Body weight (lb.) × Total bench height (ft.) ×
Stepping frequency (cycles/min.) × 1.33   (33)
Example: Work = 166 × 2 × 20 × 1.33 = 8831.2 ft.-lb. per minute*

Fixed two-step bench (Masters)

Three 11-inch (28 cm.) steps are arranged so that the subject steps up and over, turns around and climbs over again, and repeats for the desired number of trips at the desired rate. Tables 8 and 9, prepared by Masters, adjust the work load in accordance with the subject's age, sex, and weight. Table 10 lists the metronome setting for each unit derived in Tables 8 and 9. This work test is used to evaluate the exercise ECG (Chapter 7).

Adjustable two-step bench (devised by Herman Roth)

Adjustable step heights are arranged in a two-step staircase so that the subject goes up the two steps forward, then backs down. A three-beat cadence for each ascent brings both feet together at the top and at the bottom.

---

*To convert foot-pounds per minute of work rate to watts, divide by 44.2 or multiply by 0.0226.

Table 8. Standard number of ascents for males*

Weight (lb.)	Age in years												
	5-9	10-14	15-19	20-24	25-29	30-34	35-39	40-44	45-49	50-54	55-59	60-64	65-69
40-49	35	36											
50-59	33	35	32										
60-69	31	33	31										
70-79	28	32	30										
80-89	26	30	29	29	29	28	27	27	26	25	25	24	23
90-99	24	29	28	28	28	27	27	26	25	25	24	23	22
100-109	22	27	27	28	28	27	26	25	25	24	23	22	22
110-119	20	26	26	27	27	26	25	25	24	23	23	22	21
120-129	18	24	25	26	27	26	25	24	23	23	22	21	20
130-139	16	23	24	25	26	25	24	23	23	22	21	20	20
140-149	20	21	23	24	25	24	24	23	22	21	20	20	19
150-159	18	20	22	24	25	24	23	22	21	20	20	19	18
160-169	16	18	21	23	24	23	22	22	21	20	19	18	18
170-179			20	22	23	23	22	21	20	19	18	18	17
180-189			19	21	23	22	21	20	19	19	18	17	16
190-199			18	20	22	21	21	20	19	18	17	16	15
200-209				19	21	21	20	19	18	17	16	16	15
210-219				18	21	20	19	18	17	17	16	15	14
220-229				17	20	20	19	18	17	16	15	14	13

*From Masters, A. M.: The two-step test of myocardial function, Amer. Heart J. 10:495, 1935.

Table 9. Standard number of ascents for females*

Weight (lb.)	Age in years												
	5-9	10-14	15-19	20-24	25-29	30-34	35-39	40-44	45-49	50-54	55-59	60-64	65-69
40-49	35	35	33										
50-59	33	33	32										
60-69	31	32	30										
70-79	28	30	29										
80-89	26	28	28	28	28	27	26	24	23	22	21	21	20
90-99	24	27	26	27	27	26	25	24	23	22	21	20	19
100-109	22	25	25	26	26	25	24	23	22	21	20	19	18
110-119	20	23	23	25	25	24	23	22	21	20	19	18	18
120-129	18	22	22	24	24	23	22	21	20	19	19	18	17
130-139	16	20	20	23	23	22	21	20	19	19	18	17	16
140-149		18	19	22	22	21	20	19	19	18	17	16	16
150-159		17	17	21	20	20	19	19	18	17	16	16	15
160-169		15	16	20	19	19	18	18	17	16	16	15	14
170-179		13		19	18	18	17	17	16	16	15	14	13
180-189				18	17	17	17	16	16	15	14	14	13
190-199				17	16	16	16	15	15	14	13	13	12
200-209				16	15	15	15	14	14	13	13	12	11
210-219				15	14	14	14	13	13	13	12	11	11
220-229				14	13	13	13	13	12	12	11	11	10

*From Masters, A. M.: The two-step test of myocardial function, Amer. Heart J. 10:495, 1935.

Table 10. Metronome settings (MNS) per number of ascents (No.)

No.	MNS	No.	MNS
13 - 34⅔		25 - 66⅔	
14 - 37⅓		26 - 69⅓	
15 - 40		27 - 72	
16 - 42⅔		28 - 75⅔	
17 - 45⅓		29 - 78⅓	
18 - 48		30 - 81	
19 - 50⅔		31 - 83⅔	
20 - 53⅓		32 - 86⅓	
21 - 56		33 - 89	
22 - 58⅔		34 - 91⅔	
23 - 61⅓		35 - 94⅓	
24 - 64		36 - 97	

As in the stepping ergometer test, three or four submaximal work rates are chosen so that rates of work raise the heart rate to between 110 and 150 beats per minute. A straight line fitted to the plots of the heart rate against corresponding work rates gives a graphic picture of the relative fitness status of each individual.

ERGOMETRIC LOADING

Ergometer work loads can be varied in several ways, as outlined below.

Duration	Response	Study purpose
Less than 1 minute	Anaerobic	Sprint fitness
4 to 8 minutes	Aerobic	Endurance fitness, cardiopulmonary function
20 to 90 minutes	Thermal loading	Heat regulation
Over 90 minutes	Fuel and fluid depletion	Nutrition, fluid balance

The types of load are as follows:

Single-level (fixed)
> Continuous: constant load and rate of work for a fixed period (5 minutes bench stepping) or for a fixed task (running up a flight of stairs)
> Discontinuous series: intervals of work and rest (intermittent)

Increasing loads (progressive)
> Continuous: gradual increase in load at preset speed or gradual increase in speed at preset load
> Nearly continuous
>> Non–steady state levels: stepwise increase in load with increments too high or duration too brief to achieve plateaus or physiological responses
>> Steady state levels: steps of work continued long enough to achieve some degree of plateaus in physiological responses
> Discontinuous series: intervals of work and rest (intermittent)

The type of load affects the physiological responses. Selection of load patterns is made on the basis of the safety of the subject and the object of the test.

Ways of varying the intensity of work

☐ Increasing resistance (i.e., bicycle brake, treadmill grade, stepping bench height)

☐ Increasing frequency (i.e., speed of pedaling, speed of walking or running on treadmill, rate of stepping on bench)

☐ Shortening or eliminating rest periods in discontinuous work
☐ Lengthening work periods in discontinuous work

Proficiency check

Task	Date completed	Instructor's initials
1. Calibrate a mechanical bicycle ergometer.	_____	_____
2. Describe all aspects of a sample experiment using the bicycle ergometer.	_____	_____
3. Discuss or demonstrate the use of the Morehouse-Collins cardiotachimetric controller.	_____	_____
4. With the use of the treadmill, determine $\dot{V}_{O_2max}$.	_____	_____
5. Calculate $\dot{V}_{O_2}$, using the stepping ergometer as the means of obtaining raw data.	_____	_____
6. Explain the proper usage of the Harvard step test.	_____	_____
7. Using a minimum of three submaximal work rates on the two-step bench, contrast the relative fitness status of two or more test subjects.	_____	_____

Sample experiments

☐ Calibrate a stepping bench by measuring its exact platform height.

☐ Calibrate a treadmill by comparing its indicated and actual grades and speeds.

☐ Calibrate a friction bicycle ergometer by comparing its indicated and actual resistance when certified weights are suspended.

☐ Measure the chain and gear resistance on a friction bicycle ergometer and prepare a correction chart for indicated and actual work in pedaling at various speeds (40, 50, and 60 r.p.m.).

☐ Calibrate an electric bicycle ergometer at various pedal speeds and brake loads and prepare a correction chart for indicated and actual work.

☐ Using an inexpensive but well-built stationary bicycle exerciser, attach a strain gauge to the pedal mechanism to record the force of the feet against the pedals.

☐ Referring to the preceding outline, select one laboratory work device (bicycle ergometer, treadmill, or stepping bench) and observe the differences in physiological responses to two types of loading.

☐ Examine the equivalency of work load (kg.-m./min.), oxygen uptake (ml./kg./min.), and heart rate (beats/min.) in response to an exercise protocol consisting of continuous 5-minute periods of work at work loads of 488 kg.-m./min. (80 watts), 732 kg.-m./min. (120 watts), and 976 kg.-m./min. (160 watts).

☐ Reexamine the above when five continuous periods of work are performed at controlled heart rates of 100, 120, and 140 beats per minute, or controlled oxygen uptakes of 10, 17, and 24 ml./kg./min. (3, 5, and 7 MET).

☐ Measure a long flight of steps or obtain a contour map showing a road grade and convert values into work loads for subjects of various sizes climbing at various rates. Express results in kilogram-meters and watts (1 watt resistance = 6.1 kg.-m./min. work).

☐ Prepare a pacing plan to control the ascent of the above climbing course at three preset speeds, using checkpoints and a stopwatch.

☐ Compare the heart rates and oxygen consumptions of several subjects performing the above climb at the three preset speeds.

☐ Study the problem of leg fatigue in bicycle, treadmill, and stepping work.

☐ Compare fitness indices from the step test, or physiological responses to an ergometer test, with subject's age, health history, activity history, and strength measurements.

☐ Measure the effects of stepping mechanics and motivation on fitness scores.

☐ Observe heart rates and oxygen consumptions at various work load plateaus to determine the duration of work at each plateau necessary to attain near–steady state levels.

☐ Compare the heart rate responses to two ergometric protocols: one increasing 100 kg.-m./min. every 30 seconds, the other increasing 200 kg.-m./min. every minute—both starting at 200 kg.-m./min.

☐ Establish a simple test protocol on one laboratory work device (bicycle ergometer) and construct a test protocol using another device (stepping bench) which correlates well in physiological responses.

☐ Test fitness on two laboratory work load devices, train for one month by daily progressive exercise on one of the devices, and again test fitness on both devices. Note influence of specificity factor.

☐ In an experiment in which a predetermined heart rate (120 beats/min.) is maintained for 5 minutes by adjusting the work rate in high-fitness and low-fitness subjects, correlate the initial rise in heart rate with leg strength; also correlate the decrease in work rate during the fifth minute with the work rate during that period. Do these correlations suggest that two factors, power and endurance, are involved in continuous work?

REFERENCES

Balke, B., and Ware, R. W.: An experimental study of "physical fitness" of airforce personnel, U.S. Armed Forces Med. J. 10:675, 1959.

Brouha, L., Graybiel, A., and Heath, C. W.: The step test; a simple method of measuring physical fitness for hard muscular work in adult men, Rev. Canad. Biol. 2:86, 1943.

Coates, J., and Meade, F.: The energy expenditure and mechanical energy demand in walking, Ergonomics 3:97, 1960.

Morehouse, L.: Heart-controlled ergometry in cardiovascular stress testing, J. Occup. Med. 10:655, 1968.

Sloan, A.: Physical fitness and body build of young men and women, Ergonomics 12:25, 1969.

von Döbeln, W.: A simple bicycle ergometer, J. Appl. Physiol. 15:662, 1954.

Weiss, R., and Phillips, M.: Administration of tests in physical education, St. Louis, 1954, The C. V. Mosby Co.

SUGGESTED READING

Åstrand, P-O.: Ergometry—test of physical fitness, Varberg, Sweden, 1956, A. B. Cykelfabriken Monark.

Billings, C. E., Jr., et al.: Measurement of human capacity for aerobic muscular work, J. Appl. Physiol. 15:1001, 1960.

Brannon, F., Hart, J., and Eyler, M.: Intensity of treadmill training and its effects on body composition in rats, Res. Quart. Amer. Ass. Health Phys. Educ. 40:670, 1969.

Buskirk, E., et al.: Maximal performance at altitude and on return from altitude in conditioned runners, J. Appl. Physiol. 23:259, 1967.

Chiang, B., Montoye, H. J., and Cunningham, D. A.: Treadmill exercise study of healthy males in a total community—Tecumseh, Michigan—clinical and electrocardiographic characteristics, Amer. J. Epidem. 91:368, 1970.

Consolazio, C. F., Johnson, R. E., and Pecora, L. J.: Physiological measurements of metabolic functions in man, New York, 1963, McGraw-Hill Book Co.

Cumming, G., and Alexander, W.: The calibration of bicycle ergometers, Canad. J. Physiol. Pharmacol. 46:917, 1968.

Dill, D., and Montoye, H. J.: Man's capacity for consuming oxygen—comments on an article, J. Sports Med. 8:245, 1968.

Hebbelinck, M.: Ergometry in physical training research, J. Sports Med. 9:69, 1969.

Hermansen, L., and Saltin, B.: Oxygen uptake during maximal treadmill and bicycle exercise, J. Appl. Physiol. **26**:21, 1969.

Karpovich, P.: A frictional bicycle ergometer, Res. Quart. Amer. Ass. Health Phys. Educ. **21**:210, 1950.

Luft, U., et al.: Physical performance in relation to body size and composition, Ann. N. Y. Acad. Sci. **110**:795, 1963.

Mellerowicz, H.: Ergometrie, Berlin, 1962, Urban & Schwarzenberg Munchen.

Montoye, H. J., et al.: Laboratory methods of assessing metabolic capacity in a large epidemiologic study, Amer. J. Epidem. **91**:38, 1970.

Montoye, H. J., et al.: Heart rate response to a modified Harvard step test: males and females, age 10-69, Res. Quart. Amer. Ass. Health Phys. Educ. **40**:153, 1969.

Montoye, H. J., Willis, P. W., III., and Cunningham, D. A.: Heart rate response to submaximal exercise—relation to age and sex, J. Geront. **23**:127, 1968.

Perlman, L., et al.: Exercise proteinuria, Med. Sci. Sports **2**:20, 1970.

Shephard, R.: The relative merits of the step test, bicycle ergometer and treadmill in the assessment of cardiorespiratory fitness, Arbitsphysiol. **23**:219, 1966.

Shepherd, J.: The blood flow through the calf after exercise in subjects with arteriosclerosis and claudication, Clin. Sci. **9**:49, 1950.

Stoboy, H.: Physical fitness testing methods and criteria, Trans. N. Y. Acad. Sci. **30**:483, 1968.

CHAPTER 15

ENERGY EXPENDITURE

THEORY

Morehouse, L. E., and Miller, A. T., Jr.: Physiology of exercise, ed. 6, St. Louis, 1971, The C. V. Mosby Co., chap. 19.

Åstrand, P-O., and Rodahl, K.: Textbook of work physiology, New York, 1970, McGraw-Hill Book Co., chap. 13.

The human body, like any other engine, operates within the laws of physics. It obeys the law of conservation of energy; the energy that appears as work must have previously entered the body in the form of food, and if a worker expends energy above the caloric content of his food intake he will lose weight.

The body has a limited capacity for energy expenditure. The maximum rate is about two horsepower (hp), which can be maintained for only a few seconds, and the all-day activity level is about 0.2 hp. Its use of oxygen for utilization of foods is directly related to heat production and energy expenditure. The amount of oxygen consumed is directly proportional to the energy expended in physical activity. One liter of oxygen consumed is the equivalent of 5 kilocalories (kcal.) of heat production. At rest about 3.5 ml. of oxygen is used per kilogram* of body weight per minute (ml./kg./min.). For walking at 2 m.p.h. the comparable usage is about 12 ml. Doubling the walking rate to 4 m.p.h. can double the rate of oxygen uptake. The amount of oxygen used to perform an activity is referred to as the *oxygen requirement*. In addition to the indirect approach, other methods can be used to determine energy expenditure. Some of these are listed below.

Activity diary	Body fat and lean tissue loss
Activity survey (observer)	Accumulated heart rate
Distance traveled (pedometer)	Accumulated ventilation volume
Indirect heat loss	Accumulated joint rotations
Direct heat loss	Accumulated accelerations of body parts
Food intake	Accumulated force on sole of shoe

In practice, two or more of these methods are combined to document the physiological cost of physical work.

The problem of measuring human energy expenditure is not so simple as it is for mechanical engines. As noted before, excess heat from working muscles may cause the body temperature to rise and increase oxygen intake and circulatory and respiratory functions, thus adding to the total energy cost of the work. And as will be seen in the next chapter the great variety of muscles and joints within the body, which are available to perform work, results in large variations in the efficiency with which the body functions. Efficiency of the body varies from 10 to 30%, and the amount of energy expended cannot be inferred directly from the amount of useful work done unless the efficiency is known. Further complicating factors in the

---

*1 kilogram = 2.2 pounds.

measurement of human energy expenditure are the time lag of two minutes or so after the onset of work, before oxygen intake is adjusted to the new level of work, and the persistent elevated use of oxygen for several minutes after work is stopped. These and other factors to be taken up in this chapter make the measurement of physical effort and rate of working a sophisticated task.

TERMINOLOGY AND FORMULAS

gross aerobic cost of work Total amount of oxygen (or kilocalorie or kilogram-meter equivalent) required during work and recovery. See Formula 34:

$$\text{Gross cost} = \text{Work } V_{O_2} + \text{Recovery } V_{O_2} \tag{34}$$

Example, using V_{O_2} (liters): $= 20.2$ L. $+ 8.3$ L. $= 28.5$ L.

net aerobic cost of work Gross cost of work minus the resting oxygen consumption for an equivalent period of time.

$$\text{Net cost} = \text{Work } V_{O_2} \text{ (liters)} - (\text{Rest } \dot{V}_{O_2} \text{ [L./min.]}) \times \text{Minutes of work} \tag{35}$$
and recovery

$$
\begin{aligned}
\text{Example:} &= 28.5 \text{ L.} - (0.2 \text{ L./min.} \times 20 \text{ min.}) \\
&= 28.5 \text{ L.} - 4.0 \text{ L.} \\
&= 24.5 \text{ L.}
\end{aligned}
$$

physical work External mechanical work calculated by measuring force and displacement (Fs). See Formula 24.

physiological effort Man's reaction during physical activity in terms of internal functions such as metabolism, respiration, and circulation.

work rate (WR) The amount of work (kg.-m.) performed in a unit of time (min.):

$$\text{WR} = \frac{\text{kg.-m.}}{\text{min.}}$$

May also be expressed in such units as watts/min., hp, Cal./hr., BTU/hr., or equivalent expressions. See Formula 25.

steady state work A level of physical activity in which the rate of oxygen consumption $(\dot{V}_{O_2})$ corresponds to the demands of the tissues, and heart rate and pulmonary ventilation have attained stability (less than 5% deviation in one minute).

Caloric and work equivalents of one liter of oxygen as related to respiratory quotient (R.Q.). Assumes steady state activity.

R.Q.	Caloric equivalent for oxygen (per liter) (kcal.)	Work equivalent for oxygen (per liter) (kg.-m.)
0.82	4.825	2059
0.90	4.924	2090
1.00	5.047	2153

USE OF THE MET FOR CLASSIFYING EFFORT

A system for classifying physical activities utilizes the concept of "metabolic equivalents" or METS. One MET is equal to a metabolic rate of 50 kcal. per square meter per hour, or 250 ml. of oxygen per kilogram per hour, which is the approximate metabolism of a resting, sitting man.

Use of METS in the classification of physiological effort is shown in Tables 11 to 14. Tables such as these give an order of magnitude of the relative intensity of various forms of work by young men, but what is moderate work for one man may be either mild or strenuous for others. The tables do not apply generally to women or to older men, since their working capacities are usually much lower. However, the most fit women are superior to the least fit men and some highly fit men in their

Table 11. Classification of physical activities*

Classification	Industrial work time	Sports (without rest)	Occupational activities (without rest)
Very light	Above 8 hours	Croquet	Light housework
Light	4-8 hours	Bowling	House painting
Moderate	1-4 hours	Volleyball	Gardening
Heavy	30-60 minutes	Basketball	Shoveling sand
Very heavy	1-30 minutes	Mountain climbing	Chopping wood
Unduly heavy	30-60 seconds	Running	Sawing wood
Extreme	Under 30 seconds	Sprinting	Fast digging

*Data in Tables 11 to 14 are typical for a college physical education student of weight 75 kg., body surface area 1.9 m., maximum physical working capacity (PWC) 1300 kg.-m./min., for 1 minute, and maximum oxygen consumption 45 ml./kg./min. For generalized application to older, unconditioned subjects see Table 4 in the 1971 text by Morehouse and Miller: *Physiology of Exercise.*

Table 12. Classification of physical work

Classification	Ergometer Watts (sec.)	Ergometer kg.-m./min.	Treadmill % grade at 3 m.p.h.	Treadmill Speed at 6% grade	Walk-run Speed (m.p.h.)	Walk-run Mile (min.)	Walk-run 600 yd. (min.: sec.)	Cycling speed Level road (m.p.h.)
Very light	Under 50	Under 300	1	Under 2.3	Under 2	Above 30	Above 4:00	Under 8
Light	50-85	300-500	2	2.3-2.5	2-4	15-30	3:42-4:00	8-10
Moderate	85-115	500-700	3	2.5-2.7	4-6	10-15	3:02-3:42	10-12
Heavy	115-150	700-900	4	2.7-2.9	6-7.5	8-10	2:33-3:02	13
Very heavy	150-185	900-1100	5	2.9-3.1	7.5-8.5	7-8	2:21-2:33	14
Unduly heavy	185-2.5	1100-1300	6	3.1-3.3	8.5-10	6-7	2:08-2:21	15
Extreme	Above 215	Above 1300	Above 6	Above 3.3	Above 10	Under 6	Under 2:08	Over 15

sixties do heavy physical work with less physiological strain than those 30-year-old men who would be classed as low fit.

METABOLIC MANAGEMENT OF INDUSTRIAL WORK

The physiological basis of work load in industry is the kilocalorie per hour (kcal./hr.) output. The reference maximum (the most work that can be expected without injury to health) is 4800 kcal. for a 24-hour period. Of this total, 2300 kcal. is reserved for "off-work" needs (16 hours) and the remaining 2500 kcal. is considered maximum for an 8-hour work period, 2000 being the normal. For practical purposes an average of 4 kcal. per minute (or 240 kcal. per hour) is ideal for most workers as they are productive without tiring when working on a cycle of 55 minutes

Table 13. Metabolic classification of effort

Clas-sification	Lactate (mg. %)	R.Q.	$\dot{V}_{O_2}$ (L./min.)	$\dot{V}_{O_2}$ (ml./kg./min.)	METS	$\dot{V}_{O_2max}$ (%)	MR (kcal./min.)	BTU (per min.)	Temperature (°C.)
Basal	9.6	0.82	0.2	2.8			1.0	4.0	37
Rest (sitting)	9.6	0.82	0.316	4.2	1		1.58	6.32	37
Very light	Under 15	0.82-0.84	Under 0.5	Under 10	Under 2.5	Under 10	Under 3.5	Under 14	Under 37.2
Light	Under 15	0.84-0.86	0.5-1.0	10-17	2.5-5.0	10-30	3.5-5.5	14-22	Under 37.2
Moderate	15-20	0.86-0.88	1.0-1.5	17-24	5.0-7.5	30-50	5.5-8.0	22-32	37.2-37.4
Heavy	20-40	0.88-0.92	1.5-2.0	24-31	7.5-10.0	50-70	8.0-10.5	32-42	37.4-37.6
Very heavy	40-60	0.92-0.95	2.0-2.5	31-38	10.0-12.5	70-90	10.5-13.0	42-52	37.6-37.8
Unduly heavy	60-80	0.95-1.1	2.5-3.0	38-45	12.5-15.0	90-100	13.0-15.5	52-62	37.8-38.0
Extreme	Above 80	Above 1.1	Above 3.0	Above 45	Above 15.0	Above 100	Above 15.5	Above 62	Above 38.0

Table 14. Cardiopulmonary classification of effort

Classification	MV (L./min.)	f_r (breaths/min.)	f_h (beats/min.)	Blood pressure, systolic (mm. Hg)
Rest	7.2	12	60	120
Very light	Under 10	Under 14	Under 90	Under 140
Light	10-20	14-16	90-110	140-150
Moderate	20-35	16-18	110-130	150-160
Heavy	35-50	18-20	130-150	160-170
Very heavy	50-65	20-25	150-170	170-180
Unduly heavy	60-85	25-30	170-190	180-190
Extreme	Above 85	Above 30	Above 190	Above 190

of work and 5 minutes of rest. Rates of work above 4 kcal. per minute and work under any kind of stress (possibly reflected by increased heart rate) require longer and more frequent rest pauses.

USE OF WORK HEART RATE TO ASSESS PHYSIOLOGICAL COST OF MANUAL OPERATIONS

The physiological reactions to a given job can be determined by recording the heart rate of the worker. These reactions are useful in evaluating the stress level of the work and in determining the qualifications of the individual worker.

Each worker receives an information sheet detailing the reasons for the tests and their nature. If the worker does not object, the observer spends one or two days in the plant, becoming familiar with the layout and operations, and determines the sequence in which the jobs are to be studied. The worker becomes acquainted with the observer and with the routine measurements and understands what is expected of him. Such familiarization assures that the employee will work as usual and present normal physiological reactions.

The reasons for observing the physiological reactions to work are to answer such questions as the following:

1. What is the effect of environmental temperature on the physiological cost of the manual operation?
2. Does the job produce high, moderate, or low physiological reactions (Tables 13 and 14)?
3. Does the physiological strain increase as the shift progresses (from morning to afternoon)?

Physiological reactions to work as manifested by heart rate are affected by the work-rest cycle, seasonal variations, and environmental and body temperatures. The heart rate after the work period is counted three times:

> 1st — 30 seconds to 1 minute after work
> 2nd — 1½ minutes to 2 minutes after work
> 3rd — 2½ minutes to 3 minutes after work

The body temperature is measured by inserting the oral thermometer into the worker's mouth at the beginning of the rest period and reading it after the last (third) heart rate count.

The following sample data record follows the Brouha format.

SAMPLE DATA SHEET

Operator _____Example_____ Sex ___M___ Age ___24.8___
                   Name   Years

Height _____175 cm._____ Weight _____75 kg._____ Date _1/1/72_

Season _____Winter_____
                                     Summer, fall, etc.

| Time | Analysis of job | | | | Temperatures | | | | Recovery heart rate (beats/min.) | | |
| | Work cycle | | Description | | Environmental | | | Body | | | |
	Work (min.)	Rest (min.)	Work	Rest	Dry bulb (°F.)	Wet bulb (°F.)	Globe (°F.)	Oral (°F.)	1st	2nd	3rd
0900 to 0920	15	5	Lifting	Sitting	77	65	96	98.8	87	79	70

Heartbeat totals ("Leistungspulssumme")

The total number of heartbeats in a work period (e.g., 5 minutes of work at a certain task) or a 24-hour sum of heartbeats is a further criterion of physiological effort. Wear-around ECG recorders and heartbeat totalizers incorporating a cardio-tachometer and counter are available. When long periods of work are tabulated, heartbeat totals do not show short-term bursts of effort, which may have a different effect from fairly steady applications of effort.

The heartbeat total reflects quite accurately the relative effort exerted, when various modes of performing a standard task are compared, such as various pedaling rates (r.p.m.) at a fixed work rate (watts) for a fixed period (5 minutes) on a bicycle ergometer. The optimal mode would be revealed as showing the least heart-beat total for the work period.

Use of the heartbeat total for work studies presumes the absence of emotional and environmental factors unless these are systematically introduced.

Heart rate method of assessing metabolic rate

Heart rate is directly related to oxygen consumption when activities of varying levels of intensity are performed, and heart rate measures are the method of choice because of instrumentation problems in gathering oxygen consumption data during industrial work and sporting events.

The development of oxygen consumption computers to monitor metabolic rate (Fig. 12-2) permits relatively unhampered activity. These automated systems must be calibrated frequently against conventional methods (Chapter 12).

When heart rate monitoring is used to estimate metabolic rate during exercise, accuracy is gained if the subject is calibrated beforehand. A regression line between the subject's heart rate and his metabolic rate is constructed, using a bicycle ergometer and a steady state stepped exercise protocol, and making simultaneous observations of heart rate, RER, and oxygen consumption. Such regression equations will be in-validated by temperature changes, fatigue, emotional changes, or any other stress other than exercise. Thus heart rate monitoring for metabolic assessment is used with caution.

FOOD–BODY WEIGHT METHOD OF MEASURING ENERGY METABOLISM

Estimation of daily energy expenditure by the caloric value of food consumed assumes a reliable content of calories in a measured portion of food and a complete utilization (full absorption and no excretion) of foodstuffs. Since maintenance of body weight is a critical factor, it is also assumed that body fluid volume is unchanged and that muscle to fat ratio is not altered. Many foods with caloric contents marked on the can or box are available commercially. When foods are eaten uncooked and in measured portions, a fairly accurate log of food intake can be tabulated. Caloric contents of feces and urine and possibly the sweat should be measured. Body weight scales must be accurate to within 0.5 kg. Periodic determination of body fluid volume and body tissue composition is used to reveal variations affecting the body weight factor.

Tables listing caloric contents of foods are rough approximations only. Often the portions listed cannot be defined (e.g., "1 pat of butter," "1 slice of bread," "1 large egg," "2 slices of crisp bacon"). Even when weights are given, "3 ounces of broiled hamburger" does not describe the widely varying fat content.

In a like manner, tables of caloric cost of various activities are very rough approximations, since the values depend on the individual's size, skill, fitness, and the effort he puts into the activity. For example, probably no two tennis players use the same energy in an hour of play.

SAMPLE ENERGY EXPENDITURE PROTOCOL

Subject

Name _____Example_____ Sex _____Male_____ Age _____24.8_____
years

Height _____176_____ Weight _____75.0_____ Lean body mass _____157.2_____
cm. kg. kg.

Specialty or experience _____P.E. major_____

Energy expenditure

Weight (kg.)	75.0
Time (min.)	5.0
Carbon dioxide elimination (L./min.)	1.18
Oxygen consumption (L./min.)	1.25
Oxygen consumption (ml./kg./min.)	16.7
Metabolic rate (kcal./m.^{2}/hr.)	500
METS	10
Respiratory exchange ratio	0.94
Heartbeat total	923
Heart rate (beats/min.)	185
Respiratory rate (breaths/min.)	32
Minute ventilation (L./min.)	91.3
Blood lactate (mg./100 ml.)	85.0
Oxygen debt (L.)	3.2

WORK DESCRIPTION

In documenting the physiological cost of physical work it is necessary to describe the working conditions, including the physical activities performed and the environment of the work. The following outline is a guide.

Physical activities
Rest
Basal conditions
Work
Type of equipment
Type of work
Load
Frequency
Speed
Pace or work plan (spurts)
Duration
Work-rest cycle
Style or technique
Motion analysis

        Muscle analysis
        Schedule of observations
    Recovery
        Posture
        Schedule of observations
  Environment
    Social and physical
        Laboratory conditions
        Field conditions
        Competition
        Estimate of maximum effort
    Climate
        Temperature
            Dry bulb
            Wet bulb
            Globe
        Wind velocity

Proficiency check

Task	Date completed	Instructor's initials
1. Select an industrial job involving manual work and write out a method of analyzing the physiological cost of this particular form of labor.	_____	_____
2. Set up an exercise program involving activities of varying intensity levels and use heart rate measures to evaluate changes in the metabolic rate.	_____	_____

Sample experiments

☐ Correlate two or more different methods of documenting energy expenditure during a period of work.

☐ Measure the energy cost of climbing stairs, using oxygen determinations.

☐ Evaluate a work task by constructing a metabolic profile.

☐ Validate the use of the heart rate in estimating the metabolic cost of work.

REFERENCE

Brouha, L.: Physiology in industry—evaluation of industrial stresses by the physiological reactions of the worker, ed. 2, New York, 1967, Pergamon Press, Inc.

SUGGESTED READING

Banister, E., et al.: The caloric cost of playing handball, Res. Quart. Amer. Ass. Phys. Educ. **35**:236, 1964.

Banister, E., and Brown, S.: The relative energy requirements of physical activity. In Falls, H. B., editor: Exercise physiology, New York, 1968, Academic Press.

Beaver, W., and Wasserman, K.: Transients in ventilation at start and end of exercise, J. Appl. Physiol. **25**:390, 1968.

Bonjer, F.: Physical working capacity and energy expenditure. In Denolin, H., et al., editors: Ergometry in cardiology, Mannheim, 1968, Boehringer.

Buskirk, E.: An introduction to exercise and performance evaluation, J. S. Carolina Med. Ass. **65** (supp. 1):4, Dec., 1969.

Buskirk, E.: Problems related to the caloric cost of living, Bull. N. Y. Acad. Med. **36**: 365, 1960.

Cerretelli, P., Sikand, R., and Farhi, L.: Effect of increased airway resistance on ventilation and gas exchange during exercise, J. Appl. Physiol. **27**:597, 1969.

Comroe, J.: Physiology of respiration, Chicago, 1966, Year Book Medical Publishers, Inc.

Coates, J., and Meade, F.: The energy expenditure and mechanical energy demand in walking, Ergonomics **3**:97, 1960.

Dempsey, J., et al.: Work capacity determinants and physiologic cost of weight-supported work in obesity, J. Appli. Physiol. 21:181, 1966.

Falls, H.: The relative energy requirements of various physical activities in relation to physiological strain, J. S. Carolina Med. Ass. 8(supp.):8, Dec., 1969.

Falls, H., Ismail, A., and MacLeod, D.: Physical working capacity and motor fitness in relation to age of American male university faculty, J. Ass. Phys. Ment. Rehab. 20:184, 1966.

Goldman, R., and Iampietro, P.: Energy cost of load carriage, J. Appl. Physiol. 17:675, 1962.

Konishi, F.: Food energy equivalents of various activities, J. Amer. Diet. Ass. 46:186, 1965.

Michael, E., Hutton, K., and Horvath, S.: Cardiorespiratory responses during prolonged exercise, J. Appl. Physiol. 16:997, 1961.

Miles, W.: Oxygen consumption during three yoga-type breathing patterns, J. Appl. Physiol. 19:75, 1964.

Morehouse, L.: Utilisation du rythme cardiaque pour la surveillance de l'homme travaillant dans un milieu inhabituel, Kinanthropologie 2:3, 1970.

Nutritive value of foods, Home Garden Bull. 72: revised 1964, U. S. Department of Agriculture.

Sharp, J., et al.: The total work of breathing in normal and obese men, J. Clin. Invest. 43:728, 1964.

Shephard, R.: World standards of cardio-respiratory performance, Arch. Environ. Health 13:664, 1966.

Shuey, C., Pierce, A., and Johnson, R.: An evaluation of exercise tests in chronic obstructive lung disease, J. Appl. Physiol. 27:256, 1969.

Weir, J.: New methods for calculating metabolic rate with special references to protein metabolism, J. Physiol. 109:1, 1949.

Wells, J., Balke, B., and Van Fossan, D.: Lactic acid accumulation during work—a suggested standardization of work classification, J. Appl. Physiol. 10:51, 1957.

Workman, J., and Armstrong, B.: Oxygen cost of treadmill walking, J. Appl. Physiol. 18:798, 1963.

CHAPTER 16

EFFICIENCY

THEORY

Morehouse, L. E., and Miller, A. T., Jr.: Physiology of exercise, ed. 6, St. Louis, 1971, The C. V. Mosby Co., chap. 20.

Åstrand, P-O., and Rodahl, K.: Textbook of work physiology, New York, 1970, McGraw-Hill Book Co., chaps. 2, 10.

The efficiency with which man performs work is expressed as the ratio between his physiological effort and the physical work he accomplishes. Expressed as a percentage, the efficiency of the human body is between 10 and 30%. That is, between 10 and 30 units of work are performed for each 100 units of effort expended.

Efficiency of static and negative work

Efficiency at static work tasks in which no mechanical work is done, such as supporting a stationary load or walking on a level road, is evaluated in terms of oxygen consumption per unit time (minute). The more efficient worker uses less oxygen (energy). The efficiency of negative work, as in descending stairs, can be evaluated the same way. Optimal postures and the effects of environmental conditions (music) can be assessed in this manner.

The basic measure of physiological effort is oxygen consumption. From this is inferred the rate of energy expenditure, either in Calories per unit time or in watts.

The precision with which body processes function to take up oxygen during work is also a factor in efficiency. Adjustment of frequency and volume of breathing to provide required oxygen is an index of physiological efficiency. The adjustment of heart rate and stroke volume to transport oxygen from the lungs to the muscles and to move the excess heat from the muscles to the skin is a further measure of efficiency.

DEFINITIONS AND FORMULAS

$$\text{Gross efficiency} = \frac{\text{Work accomplished}}{\text{Energy expended}} = \frac{W \times 100}{E} \tag{34}$$

$$\text{Net efficiency} = \frac{\text{Work accomplished}}{\text{Energy expended above that at rest}} = \frac{W \times 100}{E - e} \tag{35}$$

$$\text{Absolute efficiency} = \frac{\substack{\text{Work accomplished} \\ \text{(e.g., in walking with load)}}}{\substack{\text{Energy expended above that in} \\ \text{walking without the load}}} = \frac{W \times 100}{E_1 - E_u} \tag{36}$$

where W = caloric equivalent of external work performed
E = gross caloric output, including resting and recovery metabolism
e = resting metabolic caloric output
E_1 = gross caloric output, loaded
E_u = gross caloric output, unloaded

steady state Body systems are functioning at a relatively steady rate; the rate of change in the variables studied is within certain limits over a period of time; for example, the heart rate between 2 and 6 minutes is less than 10 beats per minute.

Equivalencies

1 liter of oxygen $\approx$ 5 Cal.
1 Cal. = 1 kcal. = 1000 cal. $\approx$ 4 BTU $\approx$ 3086 foot-pounds
1 Cal./min. $\approx$ 0.09 hp $\approx$ 70 watts
1 watt = 0.86 kcal./hr.

MECHANICAL EFFICIENCY (E)

Mechanical (or physical) efficiency is the ratio of energy output (work) to input. Energy input is measured in terms of the energy equivalent of the oxygen cost of the work. To obtain the *net* efficiency the basal metabolic oxygen uptake is subtracted from the overall figure of oxygen consumption, as shown below. *Gross* mechanical efficiency is calculated without subtracting the basal oxygen uptake from the overall oxygen consumption (gross energy expenditure).

Calculation of net mechanical (physical) efficiency (E)

$$\text{Efficiency (E)} = \frac{\text{Work output}}{\text{Energy input}} \times 100 \tag{35}$$

$$E = \frac{\text{Rate of work (kg. - m./min.)}}{(\dot{V}_{O_2}\ [\text{L./min.}],\ \text{exercise} - \dot{V}_{O_2}\ [\text{L./min.}],\ \text{rest}) \times 5.0 \times 427} \times 100$$

where 5.0 = caloric equivalent of a liter of oxygen (R. Q. = 1.0) in kilocalories and 427 = equivalent of 1 kcal. (in kg. - m./min.)

Example

$$E = \frac{1000}{(2.38 - 0.23) \times 5.0 \times 427} \times 100$$

$$= \frac{1000}{2.15 \times 2185} \times 100$$

$$= \frac{1000}{4697.75} \times 100 = 21.3\%$$

PHYSIOLOGICAL EFFICIENCY
Oxygen pulse (O_2 pulse)

The O_2 pulse is a measure of the volume of oxygen taken up by that amount of blood which is pumped out of the right ventricle into the pulmonary circulation at each pulse beat. The volume of oxygen is determined by the amount of unloaded hemoglobin pumped to the lungs each pulse beat, and the stroke volume of the right ventricle. Since at maximum exertion the arterial-venous O_2 difference is constant, the oxygen pulse is proportional to the stroke volume. An increase in O_2 pulse at maximum work indicates an increase in stroke volume.

$$O_2 \text{ pulse} = \frac{O_2 \text{ consumption (ml./min.)}}{\text{Heart rate (beats/min.)}} \tag{37}$$

$$\text{Example: } O_2 \text{ pulse (ml.)} = \frac{3900}{195} = 20 \text{ ml.}$$

From rest to work the O_2 pulse value rises from 3.5 to 20 ml.

Work pulse (W₁₇₀)

The rate of work performed at a heart rate of 170 beats per minute with the heart rate in relatively steady state is referred to as W_{170}. Analogous symbols are W_{150} and W_{130}. The value is usually obtained by interpolation between two observed values of heart rate at given work loads. If extrapolation is used, state the distance of extrapolated values from the values known. Give the criteria of the relatively steady state. This work pulse, W_{170}, is correlated to actual physical performances, such as skiing or swimming, as well as or better than the maximal oxygen uptake. It is also highly correlated to the stroke volume of the heart and other functional and anatomical measures that influence the physical working capacity during exercise demanding a high oxygen uptake. It is a measure of the working intensity that can be maintained for various periods; 85% of W_{170} on a bicycle ergometer can be continued for 1 hour and 65% for 4 hours by healthy fit young men.

KGM/150

The physical working capacity at a 150 per minute heart rate work load in kilogram-meters per minute (KGM) is measured during work for 6 minutes at a mean heart rate, between the fifth and the sixth minute, of 150 beats per minute. KGM/150 is not affected by age but is affected by physical activity habits and by anxiety. KGM/150 is related to body size and, when used to compare individuals, the results are expressed as the performance at a heart rate of 150 per square meter of body surface (KGM/150/BSA, m.²).

In healthy subjects two consecutive loads, 300 and 450 KGM, are imposed for 6 minutes each. The mean heart rate between the fifth and the sixth minute of each load is regarded as the heart rate at that load. Subjects known to be in poor physical condition use loads of 150 and 300 kg.-m. per minute, or KGM.

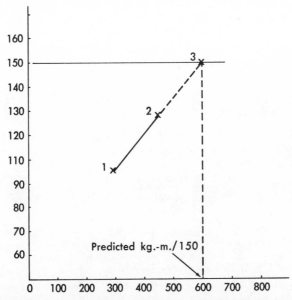

Fig. 16-1. Chart illustrating the prediction of kg.-m./150 from heart rates at work rates of 300 and 450 kg.-m. per minute (KGM).

The subject remains idle for 4 minutes while his work pulse ratio is evaluated to determine which load to apply to obtain a heart rate of 150 beats per minute. This is done by plotting on a graph paper the two heart rates observed and then interpolating or extrapolating on a straight line to a heart rate of 150 per minute to obtain the predicted KGM load. (See Fig. 16-1.)

Apply the predicted load for 6 minutes and obtain the mean heart rate during the sixth minute of work. Plot the third experimental value on the graph paper and interpolate or extrapolate to a heart rate of 150. Express the result as KGM/150 or as KGM/150/BSA, m.^{2}.

Interpretation	KGM/150	KGM/150/BSA, m.^{2}
Low	Under 700	Under 300
Average	700-800	300-400
High	Over 800	Over 400

RESPIRATORY EFFICIENCY
Ventilation equivalent for oxygen (VEO$_2$)

The ventilation/oxygen ratio indicates the amount of ventilation (VE) required per unit of oxygen consumption (Formula 38).

$$VEO_2 = \frac{\text{Ventilation (ml./min.)}_{\text{BTPS}}}{\dot{V}_{O_2} \text{ (ml./min.)}_{\text{STPD}}} \tag{38}$$

$$\text{Example: } \frac{7200 \text{ ml.}}{200 \text{ ml.}} = 36$$

If VEO$_2$ is small, respiration is more economical. As exercise proceeds in intensity from light to heavy, a level is reached at which VE increases sharply. This indicates the range of exertion at which oxygen consumption rate is becoming limited by one factor or more in the transport system, while ventilation can proceed to higher values. VE in untrained subjects at rest is typically about 23 to 25; in trained subjects, closer to 20. At near-maximum effort in exercise, VE rises above 30.

"Ventilatory equivalent" is also expressed as the volume of ventilation in liters per minute required for an oxygen consumption of 1.0 L. per minute.

VEO$_2$ is elevated during mild hyperventilation and when pulmonary function is impaired.

Respiratory equivalent (RE)

A measure of the volume of air which must be ventilated to provide for a volume of oxygen to be consumed is termed RE and is calculated as follows:

$$RE = \frac{\text{Minute volume of respiration (ml.)}}{\text{Oxygen consumption/min. (ml.)}} = \frac{MV \text{ (ml.)}}{V_{O_2}/\text{min. (ml.)}} \tag{39}$$

$$\text{Example (rest): } RE = \frac{4600}{200} = 23$$

A smaller RE indicates greater economy. At rest RE is about 23. During submaximal work RE drops, meaning that the economy of the work of breathing is increasing. At higher performances RE goes up, since MV increases at a greater rate than does $\dot{V}_{O_2}$. At maximal work load RE approaches 30.

Rate of oxygen removal

The inverse of the respiratory equivalent shows the volume (ml.) of oxygen removed by each volume (L.) of ventilation per minute (Formula 40).

$$\text{Rate of } O_2 \text{ removal} = \frac{\dot{V}_{O_2} \text{ (ml./min.)}}{\text{Ventilation (L./min.)}} \tag{40}$$

$$\text{Example: } \frac{200}{7.2} = 27.7 \text{ ml./L.}$$

During mild hyperventilation the rate of oxygen removal is reduced.

Oxygen debt (O_2 debt)

The net cost of recovery from work, known as the oxygen debt, is calculated by subtracting the preexercise resting oxygen requirement (O_2 uptake for rest)* from the total oxygen consumed during recovery (recovery O_2) (Formula 41).

Example:

$$\begin{aligned} O_2 \text{ debt} &= \text{Recovery } O_2 - (O_2 \text{ uptake for rest} \times \text{Duration of recovery [min.]}) \tag{41} \\ &= 14.0 \text{ L. } O_2 - (0.20 \text{ L./min.} \times 30 \text{ min.}) \\ &= 14.0 \text{ L} - 6.0 \text{ L.} = 8.0 \text{ L.} \end{aligned}$$

Oxygen utilization coefficient

The amount of oxygen absorbed from each liter of inspired air or the difference of oxygen in the inspired and the expired air, corrected for volume, is known as the oxygen utilization coefficient.

CARDIOVASCULAR EFFICIENCY
Total heart pulse (Leistungspulssumme)

The total number of heartbeats in the work period (e.g., 6 minutes at a certain load) is the total heart pulse.

Pulse deficit index (PDI)

The PDI indicates the degree to which the number of heartbeats in the first 4 minutes of work falls short of the number observed for 4 minutes after the full adjustment of the heart rate to the load has been completed, usually after 4 minutes of work at a constant load. As work load is progressively increased, the pulse deficit rises abruptly at a certain point, usually coinciding with the specific ventilation index (SVI), to be explained later. The boundary value of oxygen consumption at which the PDI changes during exercise correlates highly with the maximum oxygen intake capacity and thus is a reliable measure of physical fitness.

Recovery pulse sum (RPS)

The RPS equals the total heartbeats in the first 4 minutes of recovery from exercise, minus four times the resting heart rate. Use as an index depends on standardization of a level of work load and duration.

---

*If preexercise rate is not recorded, take resting rate to be the steady state level reached during the last period of recovery.

Individual limit of physiological compensation for increased exercise (LPC)

Physiological responses to exercise of progressively graded intensity are linear to a heart rate level of 140 to 160, depending on physical fitness, and then become nonlinear. The ratios of respiratory frequency, minute volume of ventilation, carbon dioxide production, and respiratory exchange increase, and oxygen consumption and systolic blood pressure decrease. The response curves become biphasic at about the same level of work and heart rate, indicating that the change in responses is due to a common mechanism, such as the failure of the heart to increase its stroke volume in compensatory amounts. Since the point at which the slope becomes biphasic varies with the fitness of individuals, this limit of physiological compensation (LPC) shows promise as a potential submaximal test of cardiopulmonary functional status. The mechanism of the biphasic phenomenon needs to be elucidated. Methods of continuous or near-continuous computation of the physiological variables during exercise make such studies possible.

Specific ventilation index (SVI)

A boundary value of oxygen consumption exists, at which minute volume of ventilation changes during exercise. During work at progressively increasing intensity, that oxygen level beyond which the rate of increase of ventilation per unit increase in oxygen intake shows a sharp rise is termed the "specific ventilation index" (SVI).

Proficiency check

Task	Date completed	Instructor's initials
1. Determine W_{170} and KGM/150 for a test subject.	_____	_____
2. Using data obtained from an open-circuit collection during exercise, calculate the following:		
MV	_____	_____
V_{O_2}	_____	_____
O_2 debt	_____	_____
O_2 pulse	_____	_____
VEO_2	_____	_____
RE	_____	_____
3. Calculate the gross, net, and absolute efficiency of a subject.	_____	_____
4. Measure the following items during an exercise and recovery run:		
PDI	_____	_____
RPS	_____	_____
LPC	_____	_____
SVI	_____	_____

Sample experiments

☐ Evaluate man as a source of power for continuous work in terms of cost of food intake and wage rates.

☐ Compute the quantity (liters) and flow rates of oxygen required by a man working at various tasks for 4 hours.

☐ Measure the effects of the following on mechanical efficiency:

Training	Rate of work
Altitude	Motivation
Warming-up exercise	Body size
Cold	Age
Heat	Sex
Body mechanics	

☐ Investigate the effect of rest pauses, body mechanics, or training on physiological responses to standard work loads, using various indices of efficiency.

☐ Correlate the influence of body movements on venous inflow with respiratory efficiency.

SUGGESTED READING

Allard, C., and Goulet, C.: Physical working capacity in a French-Canadian population —an epidemiological study, Forsvarsmedicin **3:**209, 1967.

Bartels, H. E., Beicherl, C. W., Hertz, G. R., and Schwab, M.: Methods in pulmonary physiology, translated by J. M. Workman, New York, 1963, Hafner Publishing Co.

Bevegård, S., Freyschuss, U., and Strandell, T.: Circulatory adaptation to arm and leg exercise in supine and sitting position, J. Appl. Physiol. **21:**37, 1966.

Cunningham, D., and Faulkner, J.: The effect of training on aerobic and anaerobic metabolism during a short exhaustive run, Med. Sci. Sports **1:**65, 1969.

Davis, H., Faulkner, T., and Miller, C.: Work physiology, Hum. Factors **11:**157, 1969.

Ekelund, L.: Circulatory and respiratory adaptation during prolonged exercise in the supine and sitting position, Acta Physiol. Scand. **70:** 88, 1967.

Knehr, C., Dill, D., and Neufeld, W.: Training and its effects on man at rest and at work, Amer. J. Physiol. 136:148, 1942.

Stoboy, H.: Physical fitness testing methods and criteria, Trans. N. Y. Acad. Sci. **30:** 483, 1968.

Whipp, B., Seard, C., and Wasserman, K.: Oxygen deficit–oxygen debt relationships and efficiency of anaerobic work, J. Appl. Physiol. **28:**452, 1970.

Whipp, B., and Wasserman, K.: Efficiency of muscular work, J. Appl. Physiol. **26:**644, 1969.

CHAPTER 17

AEROBIC CAPACITY

THEORY

Morehouse, L. E., and Miller, A. T., Jr.: Physiology of exercise, ed. 6, St. Louis, 1971, The C. V. Mosby Co., chaps. 15, 16, 18, 24, 26, 27.

Åstrand, P-O., and Rodahl, K.: Textbook of work physiology, New York, 1970, McGraw-Hill Book Co., chaps. 9, 18, Appendix.

In muscular work lasting more than 6 minutes at rates in which anaerobic sources of energy are not exceeded, there exists a highest level of work at which the body's maximum capacity to supply oxygen is reached. This level of maximum oxygen intake ($\dot{V}_{O_{2max}}$) is observed after progressively increasing the load until it exceeds the capacity for oxygen uptake and depends for its higher progression, or final spurt, on anaerobic sources of power (Chapter 18). When the rate of oxygen intake does not increase any more although work is able to be continued to higher levels for a short while longer because of anaerobic power sources, a plateau of maximum oxygen uptake known as the aerobic capacity has been reached. (See Fig. 17-1.)

Maximum oxygen uptake is limited by the capacity of the circulatory and respiratory systems to supply oxygen to the working muscles. For this reason maximum oxygen uptake is a measure of *cardiorespiratory fitness*. It is also a standard measure of *physical fitness* and a measure of impairment due to cardiovascular disease, bed rest, or other conditions.

CRITERION OF MAXIMALITY

The criterion for attainment of $\dot{V}_{O_{2max}}$ is that the oxygen consumption must cease to increase linearly with rising work loads. Since $\dot{V}_{O_{2max}}$ is a plateau value that cannot be increased by further increase in work load, the level at which no further rise in oxygen consumption occurs is scored as the maximum oxygen uptake ($\dot{V}_{O_{2max}}$).

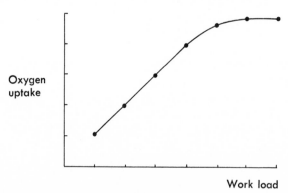

Fig. 17-1. Graph of work load versus oxygen uptake that illustrates the point of maximum oxygen uptake.

Under test conditions values from at least three determinations of oxygen rate at plateau level should agree within ± 5% (or be within 150 ml./min. or 2.1 ml./kg./min.) of each other. The highest rate is taken as the $\dot{V}_{O_{2max}}$ value.

DEFINITIONS, DIMENSIONS, AND RELATION TO VARIABLES

aerobic power Muscle power (energy per unit time) sustained by oxidative processes. Aerobic power is influenced by the different components of the oxygen transport system (lung, blood, heart, and enzyme systems) and is probably the main limiting factor in work in which the maximum effort lasts from a minute to an hour.

maximum aerobic power ($\dot{W}_{max}$) Rate of work performed at the moment when maximum oxygen consumption is stabilized during exercise of increasing severity.

maximum oxygen consumption ($\dot{V}_{O_{2max}}$) Highest oxygen uptake that a healthy person can attain during exhaustive ("maximal") muscular exercise of approximately 6 minutes duration, when breathing air at approximately sea level and working on a treadmill, stepping bench, or bicycle ergometer or performing similar types of exercise activating large muscle groups. The maximum oxygen uptake is also termed *aerobic capacity*.

oxygen uptake At STPD (in L./min. and ml./kg./min.)*

physical fitness Ability to perform muscular work satisfactorily under specified conditions. In defining fitness, three types of performance are distinguished: (1) maximum attainable oxygen consumption in short, intense exercise involving large muscle groups; (2) endurance measured by the limits or breakdown of a steady state of respiratory, cardiovascular, and metabolic functions during work for a long time; (3) maximum strength in isometric contractions.

pulmonary ventilation At BTPS (in L./min.)

rate of work (in watts, N_m./min., or kpm./min.)

There is for each individual a measurable upper limit of oxygen uptake, which correlates with ability to do work. This depends on body build and composition and is affected by other factors, in the following pattern.

1. *Sex:* Is lower in women.
2. *Age:* Varies inversely with age ($r = 0.43$). The maximum oxygen uptake of the 75-year-old man is only one half that of a 17-year-old youth; yet boys and girls of 13 to 16 do not change $\dot{V}_{O_{2max}}$ by training.
3. *Size:* Varies directly with stature (height) and body surface area.
4. *Weight:* Varies directly with body weight.
5. *Lean body mass:* $\dot{V}_{O_{2max}}$ correlates 0.63 with body weight, 0.85 with fat-free body weight, and 0.91 with active tissue mass.
6. *Bed rest:* Is reduced 17% by enforced bed rest for 3 weeks.
7. *Semistarvation:* Is reduced 37% by prolonged semi-starvation.
8. *Altitude:* Is reduced 26% at an altitude of 4000 m.
9. *Geography:* Is lower in residents of temperate or tropical areas than at circumpolar regions.

Maximum oxygen intake is not dependent (varies less than 5%) on the variables listed below.

1. *Food:* Ingestion of a small meal (750 Cal.).
2. *Heat:* Exposure to heat stress up to 90° F.
3. *Warm-up:* Duration of warm-up exercise can vary.
4. *Speed of exercise:* Work rate can be slow, moderate, or fast.
5. *Repetition:* Retests show similar results.

---

*When *relative* values are given, state also some *absolute* value (e.g., body weight).

Maximum oxygen intake can be increased by physical conditioning or decreased by inactivity. The limiting factors may be one or a combination of the following.

1. The capacity of the respiratory and circulatory systems to take up and transport oxygen, which is dependent on the alveolar ventilation, the diffusing capacity of the lungs, and the capacity of the blood flow for transporting oxygen from the lungs to the capillaries
2. The capacity of the working muscles for receiving and using oxygen

DIRECT METHOD FOR MEASUREMENT OF AEROBIC CAPACITY

Direct measurement of the maximum capacity of the aerobic oxidative mechanism requires a period of exercise at very close to maximum intensity. Full oxygen consumption is not reached for a minute or longer after the metabolic rate exceeds the oxygen intake capacity.

To obtain the plateau of oxygen uptake necessary to ascertain that the maximum consumption has been reached, the subject reaches a condition very near exhaustion. This brief test does not stress the cardiovascular and pulmonary system adequately to evaluate cardiopulmonary fitness.

Maximum oxygen consumption changes somewhat with the type of exercise and the time of performance.

To compensate for the fact that oxygen uptake capacity is directly related to the size of the individual, values are expressed relative to body weight—for example, as milliliters of oxygen consumed per kilogram of body weight per minute (ml./kg./min.).

Slightly greater $\dot{V}_{O_{2max}}$ values are obtained while working on a treadmill than on a stepping bench (where they are 3.4% lower) or on a bicycle ergometer (6.6% lower). The lower values on the bicycle may be due to a pedal rate (50 r.p.m.) that is too slow. A pedal frequency of 70 r.p.m. during the final period of maximum work prevents leg fatigue and employs more widespread muscular effort.

Equipment

- [ ] Treadmill, stepping bench, or bicycle ergometer
- [ ] Metronome or acoustical timer
- [ ] Stopwatch
- [ ] Continuous oxygen consumption meter, or collection bags and gas analyzer (Chapters 11 and 12)
- [ ] Electrocardiograph with oscilloscopic display and cardiotachometer
- [ ] Blood pressure measuring apparatus

Procedure for direct measurement of $\dot{V}_{O_{2max}}$

Exercise schedule (bicycle ergometer)

See schedule at top of following page.

Oxygen rate determination protocol

USING CONTINUOUS OXYGEN CONSUMPTION RATE APPARATUS. After warm-up exercise and while the subject rests in a chair, attach the apparatus and check the system. Monitor and record oxygen rates continuously throughout loading and final periods of exercise until a definite plateau of uptake appears.

USING GAS SAMPLING TECHNIQUE. Commencee 30-second collections of expired air in sampling containers as soon as the exercise heart rate approaches 90% of the

Exercise schedule (bicycle ergometer)

Approximate time period (min.)	Activity	Description or instructions
5	Warm-up exercise	Work at 50 watts, or 300 kg.-m./min.
3	Rest	Sit in chair or remain seated on bicycle ergometer with feet elevated
5+	Exercise to 90% MEHR* ("loading" period)	Work at 50 watts or 300 kg.-m./min. for 1 minute; then with load increased by 25 watts or 150 kg.-m./min. during the first 10 seconds of every minute until 90% MEHR* is reached or until fatigue is first observed
2+	Exercise to maximum limit ("final" period)	Work with load increased by 10 watts or 60 kg.-m./min. every 30 seconds until V_{O_2} plateau is attained or until signal indicating near-exhaustion is given
3	Rest	Recline

*MEHR = Maximum exercise heart rate.

estimated maximum rate, or when the subject shows the first sign of fatigue. Continue collections in close succession during the final period until the subject exhausts.

Treadmill schedule for subject

WARM-UP EXERCISE. Walk at 3 m.p.h. on a 5% grade for 5 minutes.

LOADING EXERCISE. Run at 7.0 m.p.h., starting at the 5% grade for 1 minute and advancing to the grade which will produce a 90% maximal heart rate. This target grade is estimated from the indirect (submaximal) method. The grade is advanced in four 1-minute steps, starting at 5% and increasing in equal increments until the target grade is reached. For example, if the target grade is 20%, the equal increments are $\frac{20-5}{4} = 3.75$; so the first step is 5%, and the second, third, fourth, and fifth steps are 8.75%, 12.5%, 16.25%, and 20%.

FINAL EXERCISE. Continue running at 7.0 m.p.h., with the grade being advanced 1% every 30 seconds, until the oxygen uptake plateau is established or until a signal indicating near-exhaustion is given.

Procedure for maximal test of aerobic power ($\dot{V}_{O_{2\,max}}$)

☐ Subject, dressed for exercise, rests for 15 minutes in sitting position and observes performance of previous participant or receives instructions and observes demonstration.

☐ Personal data are recorded.

☐ Oral temperature, electrocardiogram, heart rate, and blood pressures are evaluated (see rejection criteria, Chapter 2).

☐ Body weight is recorded to nearest 0.5 kg.

☐ Subject then proceeds to do the following:

☐ Perform 5-minute warm-up exercise.

☐ Rest for 3 minutes in a chair or remaining seated on bicycle ergometer with feet elevated.

☐ Perform maximum test of aerobic power.

☐ Rest for 3 minutes in bed.

Gas sampling schedule

☐ Flush the gas collection apparatus twice during the first 2 minutes of the loading period.

☐ Collect exhaled air between 3 minutes and 30 seconds and 4 minutes of the loading period. Draw two samples for duplicate determinations.

☐ Collect exhaled air between 4 minutes and 30 seconds and 5 minutes of the loading period. Draw two samples for duplicate determinations.

☐ Collect 30-second samples of expired air in close succession throughout the final period. Draw two samples from each collection for duplicate determinations.

Cardiovascular monitoring

The electrocardiogram is monitored continuously on the oscilloscope, and the test is halted if unusual changes occur (Chapter 2). Strip chart records of the ECG are made during the final 10 seconds of each minute during the entire test, including the 3-minute recovery.

Heart rate and blood pressure are recorded during the last 20 seconds of each minute. If accurate blood pressure readings are desired, stop the exercise momentarily while the measurements are obtained.

Test conditions

Record the room temperature, humidity, barometric pressure, body position, time of day, and composition of inspired gas.

INDIRECT METHODS FOR ESTIMATION OF $\dot{V}_{O_{2max}}$ FROM SUBMAXIMAL EXERCISE TESTS

If the oxygen consumption and heart rate are exactly known at a work level that is close to the onset of substantial anaerobic work, about 75% max, the value of maximum oxygen consumption can be derived. The work level should be at a

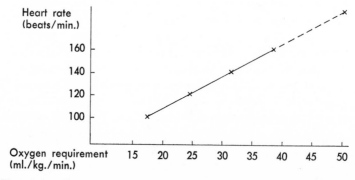

Fig. 17-2. Plot of the effect of increasing exercise on heart rate versus oxygen uptake per unit body weight.

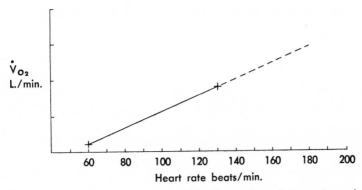

Fig. 17-3. Estimation of maximum oxygen uptake from submaximum values of oxygen uptake versus heart rate.

heart rate of 130 to 140 per minute. By this method a reasonable approximation of $\dot{V}_{O_{2max}}$ (error variance of 8 to 15%) can be achieved in well-trained young athletes performing in a cool environment. However, the method underestimates the true value in sedentary healthy adults and in persons working in hot environments or in emotionally charged states.

The submaximal tests are useful under the following circumstances:

☐ In sedentary individuals who are unwilling to perform exercise of maximum intensity

☐ When medical supervision is not available

☐ When the examinee's physical condition is not well known

☐ As the basis for calculating percentages of aerobic power prior to maximal testing

☐ As a basis for prescribing exercise for cardiopulmonary development or endurance training

Assumptions

Estimation of $\dot{V}_{O_{2max}}$ from responses to submaximal effort is based on the following principles:

1. In simple continuous physical activities such as stepping on and off a bench, cycling, or walking and running on slopes at different work rates the heart rate is a linear function of the oxygen consumption (Fig. 17-2).
2. Maximum oxygen consumption occurs at near-maximal limits of heart rate.
3. Maximum heart rate declines about 1 beat per minute per year after age 20. At age 20 the maximum heart rate is about 200 per minute.
4. Maximal heart rate declines about 1 beat per minute per 100 m. altitude.
5. If heart rate is plotted against oxygen consumption on a graph and a straight line is fitted to the points during rest and exercise, that line can be extrapolated to the individual's maximal heart rate and oxygen consumption (Fig. 17-3).

Estimation of $\dot{V}_{O_{2max}}$ (ml./kg./min.) from 12-minute run (Cooper)

Equipment

☐ Stopwatch

☐ 440-yard track

Table 15. Levels of aerobic fitness in relation to the 12-minute run and $\dot{V}_{O_2max}$ (Cooper)

Distance		$\dot{V}_{O_2max}$ (ml./kg./min.)	Fitness level for Air Force (males under 30)*
Miles	Kilometers		
Less than 1	Less than 1.61	Less than 25.0	Very poor
1.0-1.24	1.61-1.99	25.0-33.7	Poor
1.25-1.49	2.00-2.39	33.8-42.6	Fair
1.50-1.74	2.40-2.80	42.7-51.5	Good
1.75 or more	2.81 or more	51.6 or more	Excellent

*Classification for males under 30. For females and for males in age groups above 30 years see Table 16. Example: Male subject age 40 runs 1.4 miles in 12 minutes, so $\dot{V}_{O_2max}$ (ml./kg./min.) is about 38. Since the Cooper chart is for males under 30, refer to Table 16 for classification in a general population, which is seen to be "average."

Subject qualifications

☐ Healthy
☐ Nonobese
☐ Well-motivated

Procedure

☐ Measure the distance which the subject can walk or run as fast as possible in 12 minutes.
☐ Find estimated $\dot{V}_{O_2max}$, using the data in Table 15.

Estimation of $\dot{V}_{O_2max}$ from heart rate during stepping on adjustable bench (Wyndam)

Equipment

☐ Variable-height stepping bench, adjustable between 10 and 45 cm.
☐ Metronome
☐ Stopwatch
☐ Electrocardiograph or stethoscope and stopwatch
☐ Body weight scales

Procedure

☐ Record nude body weight.
☐ Adjust stepping bench to give a work rate of approximately 82 watts (494 kg.-m./min.), using the following formula:

$$x \text{ (cm.)} = \frac{49,400}{24 \times \text{wt. (kg.)}} \tag{29}$$

☐ Set the metronome at 48 beats per minute, one beat for stepping up and one for stepping down.
☐ Subject steps at 24 mounts per minute for 10 minutes, onto and off the bench.
☐ Measure the heart rate over 1 full minute during the last minute of exercise.
☐ Use the heart rate value to calculate the maximum oxygen consumption rate according to the following formula:

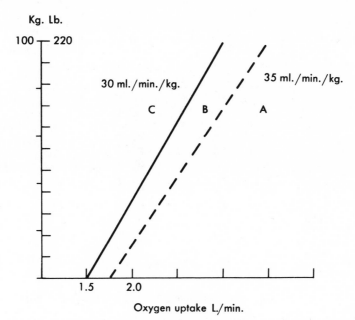

Fig. 17-4. Plot of oxygen uptake versus body weight for use in fitness classifications.

$$\text{Estimated maximum oxygen intake (L./min.)} = \frac{231}{\text{Heart rate} - 50} \qquad (42)$$

☐ Plot the estimated oxygen intake against body weight on a graph, as in Fig. 17-4.

☐ The results obtained from the graph classify individuals into "A," "B," and "C" categories as follows:

Category	Maximum oxygen consumption (ml./kg./min.)
A	Above 35
B	30-35
C	Less than 30

Estimation of $\dot{V}_{O_{2max}}$ (ml./kg./min.) from multistage treadmill performance (McDonough and Bruce)

Equipment

☐ Treadmill
☐ Clock

Procedure

☐ Subject walks to exhaustion on a motor-driven treadmill, without support of a handrail and with the work load being increased every 3 minutes as follows:

Stage	Minutes	Speed k.p.m.	Speed m.p.h.	Grade Percent	Grade Degrees
I	1-3	2.74	1.7	10	5°43'
II	4-6	4.02	2.5	12	6°51'
III	7-9	5.47	3.4	14	7°58'
IV	10-12	6.76	4.2	16	9°06'
V	13-15	8.05	5.0	18	10°12'
VI	16-18	8.85	5.5	20	11°19'
VII	19-21	9.66	6.0	22	12°25'

Table 16. Classification of aerobic capacity, $\dot{V}_{O_{2max}}$ (ml./kg./min.) STPD

Age group (years)	Male					Female				
	Very low	Low fair	Average	High good	Very high	Very low	Low fair	Average	High good	Very high
12-17	34	39	44	49	54	30	35	40	45	50
18-23	34	39	44	49	54	28	33	38	43	48
24-29	32	37	42	47	52	26	31	36	41	46
30-35	30	35	40	45	50	24	29	34	39	44
36-41	28	33	38	43	48	22	27	32	37	42
42-47	26	31	36	41	46	20	25	30	35	40
48-53	24	29	34	39	44	18	23	28	33	38
54-59	22	27	32	37	42	16	21	26	31	36
60 and +	20	25	30	35	40	14	19	24	29	34

☐ Use this regression formula:

$$\dot{V}_{O_{2max}} \text{ (ml./kg./min.)} = 3.26 \times \text{(minutes)} + 6.14 \tag{43}$$

to estimate the maximum oxygen uptake. For example, subject exercises for 10 minutes, so $\dot{V}_{O_{2max}} = 3.26 \times 10 + 6.14 = 32.6 + 6.14 = 38.74$ ml./kg./min.).

☐ Refer to Table 16 to classify the subject's aerobic capacity. Example, for male subject of age 40 and $\dot{V}_{O_{2max}}$ 38.74, classification is "average" aerobic capacity.

Proficiency check

Task	Date completed	Instructor's initials
1. Using the bicycle ergometer, measure $\dot{V}_{O_{2max}}$.		
2. Determine $\dot{V}_{O_{2max}}$ by means of the gas sampling technique used in conjunction with the treadmill as an exercise device.		
3. Describe the use of submaximal exercise testing for estimation of $\dot{V}_{O_{2max}}$.		
4. Estimate $\dot{V}_{O_{2max}}$ by use of the Cooper method.		
5. Use the Wyndam adjustable-bench method to obtain data. For estimation of $\dot{V}_{O_{2max}}$ (ml./kg./min.) and classify the subject into A, B, or C category.		
6. Describe the multistage treadmill method of estimation of $\dot{V}_{O_{2max}}$.		

Sample experiments

☐ Examine the validity of the premise that heart rate, oxygen consumption rate, and work rate have a linear relationship with each other at near-maximum levels of work.

☐ Examine the validity of the premise that the variability of maximum heart rate among individuals at a certain age is sufficiently small for the population mean to be used in individual testing without introducing a significant error.

SAMPLE DATA SHEET

Subject	Age (yr.)	Occupation	Body weight (kg.)	Fat-free body weight (kg.)	Maximum pulmonary capacity (L./min.) BTPS	Maximum oxygen uptake (L./min.)	Maximum oxygen uptake (ml./kg./min.)
Example	24	P. E. major	75	66.8	161.5	3.75	50.0

Maximum heart rate (A) (beats/ min.)	Heart rate at $\dot{V}_{O_2max}$ (B) (beats/ min.)	$\dfrac{B \times 100}{A}$ (%)					
197	186	94.4					

☐ Compare $\dot{V}_{O_2max}$ scores with various body compositions and muscular performance (Chapter 3).

☐ Study the effect of diet (vegetarian) or drugs on $\dot{V}_{O_2max}$.

☐ What is the effect of a rapid growth spurt on the $\dot{V}_{O_2max}$ of adolescents?

☐ Relate $\dot{V}_{O_2max}$ to various indices of health (Chapter 1) and performance (Chapter 7).

☐ Study the effects of seasonal variations ("spring fever") and circadian rhythms (time zone changes in jet travel) on $\dot{V}_{O_2max}$.

☐ Relate resting heart rate and other basal functions to $\dot{V}_{O_2max}$.

☐ Study day-to-day variability of ratios of heart rate to oxygen consumption rate to work rate in a small group of subjects.

☐ What is the effect of the warm-up exercise on maximum oxygen consumption scores?

☐ What is the effect of body heat storage resulting from prolonged exercise (over 10 min.) on maximum oxygen consumption?

☐ What is the effect of neglecting the cost of work of descending on an indirect estimation of $\dot{V}_{O_2max}$ in submaximal exercise tests using a stepping bench?

☐ What is the effect of pedal speed on $\dot{V}_{O_2max}$ tests using a bicycle ergometer?

☐ What is the effect of habituation on $\dot{V}_{O_2max}$ test scores using various ergometers?

☐ Examine the degree of error in estimating $\dot{V}_{O_2max}$ resulting from short (20 sec.) and long (1 full minute) counts of heart rate during a test exercise.

☐ Relate intensity of habitual physical activity (Chapter 8) to $\dot{V}_{O_2max}$.

☐ Compare the $\dot{V}_{O_2max}$ on tests using single and double stepping benches (Chapter 14).

☐ Study $\dot{V}_{O_2max}$ changes in various types of physical training.

☐ Study the effect of a prolonged (10 min.) cold shower bath, taken immediately before the test, on $\dot{V}_{O_2max}$.

☐ Study the effect of an hour's bed rest before the $\dot{V}_{O_2max}$ test.

☐ Study the effect of massage or vibrator treatments on $\dot{V}_{O_2max}$.

☐ Study the effect of abdominal ice pack on $\dot{V}_{O_2max}$.

☐ Study the effect of using handrails during treadmill and step bench tests on $\dot{V}_{O_2max}$.

☐ Study environmental effects (heat, humidity, wind speed, barometric pressures) on $\dot{V}_{O_2max}$.

☐ Examine the biological variables that may be associated with differences in $\dot{V}_{O_2max}$ in men and women.

☐ Compare the effects of adjusting the step height to adjustment of stepping rate in $\dot{V}_{O_2max}$ testing, using the following formulas:

$$\text{Step height (cm.)} = \frac{\text{Work load (kg.-m./min.)} \times 10 \text{ min.}}{\text{Body weight (kg.) Stepping rate (mounts/min.)}} \qquad (29)$$

$$\text{Stepping rate (mounts/min.)} = \frac{\text{Work load (kg.-m./min.)} \times 10 \text{ min.}}{\text{Body weight (kg.)} \times \text{Step height (cm.)}} \qquad (30)$$

REFERENCES

Cooper, K., Gey, G., and Bottenberg, R.: Effects of cigarette smoking on endurance performance, J. A. M. A. 203:189, 1968.

Döbeln, W., von, Åstrand, I., and Bergström, A.: An analysis of age and other factors related to maximal oxygen uptake, J. Appl. Physiol. 22:934, 1967.

McArdle, W. D., Magel, J. R., and Kyvallos, L.: Aerobic capacity, heart rate and estimated energy cost during women's competitive basketball, Res. Quart. Amer. Ass. Health Phys. Educ. 42:178, 1971.

Metz, K., and Alexander, J.: Estimation of maximal oxygen intake from submaximal work parameters, Res. Quart. Amer. Ass. Health Phys. Educ. 42:187, 1971.

Wyndham, C., and Strydom, N.: A code of practice for the selection and classification of members of rescue teams according to their physical working capacity, Research Report of the Johannesburg Chamber of Mines (Union of S. Africa), No. 14, 1968.

SUGGESTED READING

Allard, C., and Goulet, C.: Physical working capacity in a French-Canadian population—an epidemiological study, Forsvarsmedicin 3:209, 1967.

Andersen, K., Hellstrom, B., and Eide, R.: Strenuous muscular exertion in the polar climate, Ergonomics 11:261, 1968.

Åstrand, I.: Aerobic work capacity in men and women, with special reference to age, Acta Physiol. Scand. 49:83, 1960.

Åstrand, I., Åstrand, P-O., and Rodahl, K.:

Maximal heart rate during work in older men, J. Appl. Physiol. 14:562, 1959.

Åstrand, I., and Kilborn, Å.: Physical demands on cabin personnel in civil aviation, Aerospace Med. 40:885, 1969.

Åstrand, P-O.: Experimental studies of physical working capacity in relation to sex and age, Copenhagen, 1952, Enjar Munksgaard.

Åstrand, P-O.: Work tests with the bicycle ergometer, Varberg, Sweden, Monark-Crescent AB.

Åstrand, P-O., and Rhyming, I.: A nomogram for calculation of aerobic capacity (physical fitness) from pulse rate during submaximal work, J. Appl. Physiol. 7:218, 1954.

Åstrand, P-O., and Saltin, B.: Oxygen uptake during the first minutes of heavy muscular exercise, J. Appl. Physiol. 16:971, 1961.

Balke, B.: A test of physical performance based on the cardiovascular and respiratory responses to gradually increased work, Randolph Air Force Base, Texas, 1952, USAF School of Aviation.

Balke, B., et al.: Work capacity after blood donation, J. Appl. Physiol. 7:231, 1954.

Binkhorst, R., and van Leeuwen, P.: A rapid method for the determination of aerobic capacity, Arbeitsphysiologie 19:459, 1963.

Bruce, R., Hornsten, T., and Blackmon, J.: Myocardial infarction after normal responses to maximal exercise, Circulation 38:552, 1968.

Buskirk, E. R., et al.: Maximal performance at altitude and on return from altitude in conditioned runners, J. Appl. Physiol. **23**: 259, 1967.

Cassals, D., and Morse, M.: Cardiopulmonary data for children and young adults, Springfield, Ill., 1962, Charles C Thomas, Publisher.

Costill, D., and Fox, E.: Energetics of marathon running, Sci. Med. Sports **1**:81, 1969.

Denolin, H., et al., editors: Rehabilitation of non-coronary heart disease, Brussels, Belgium, 1969, International Society of Cardiology.

Doan, A., et al.: Myocardial ischemia after maximal exercise in healthy men, Amer. Heart J. **69**:11, 1965.

Ekelund, L.: Circulatory and respiratory adaptation during prolonged exercise, Acta Physiol. Scand. **70**:292, 1967.

Falls, H.: Development of a criterion for physical fitness tests, Washington, D. C., 1964, American Association of Health, Physical Education and Recreation National Convention.

Falls, H., Ismail, A., and MacLeod, D.: Physical working capacity and motor fitness in relation to age of American male university students, J. Ass. Phys. Ment. Rehab. **20**:184, 1966.

Glassford, R.: Comparison of maximal oxygen intake values determined by predicted and actual method, J. Appl. Physiol. **20**:509, 1965.

van Graan, C., and Greyson, J.: A comparison between the bicycle ergometer and the step-test for determining maximum oxygen intake on Kalahari bushmen, Int. Z. Angew. Physiol. **28**:344, 1970.

Grimby, G.: Maximal exercise tests in middle-aged men. In Denolin, H., et al., editors: Ergometry in cardiology, Brussels, Belgium, 1967, International Society of Cardiology.

Hanson, J.: Comparative exercise cardiorespiratory response of normal men in third, fourth and fifth decades of life, Circulation **37**:345, 1968.

Hermansen, L., and Saltin, B.: Oxygen uptake during maximal treadmill and bicycle exercise, J. Appl. Physiol. **26**:31, 1969.

Holmgren, A., et al.: Effect of training on work capacity, total hemoglobin, blood volume, heart volume and pulse rate in upright and recumbent position, Acta Physiol. Scand. **50**:72, 1960.

Ishiko, T.: Aerobic capacity and external criteria of performance, Canad. Med. Ass. J. **96**:746, 1967.

Kasch, F., et al.: A step test for inducing maximal work, J. Ass. Phys. Ment. Rehab. **19**:84, 1965.

Knuttgen, H.: Aerobic capacity of adolescents, J. Appl. Physiol. **22**:655, 1967.

MacNab, R., Conger, P., and Taylor, P.: Differences in maximal and submaximal work capacity in men and women, J. Appl. Physiol. **27**:644, 1969.

Magel, J. R., and Faulkner, J. A.: Maximal oxygen uptakes of college swimmers, J. Appl. Physiol. **22**:929, 1967.

Margaria, R.: Commentary, Canad. Med. Ass. J. **96**:734, 1967.

Margaria, R.: Exercise at altitude, New York, 1967, Excerpta Medica Foundation.

Margaria, R., Aghemo, P., and Rovelli, E.: Indirect determination of maximal O_2 consumption in man, J. Appl. Physiol. **20**:1070, 1965.

McDonough, J., and Bruce, R.: Maximal exercise testing in assessing cardiovascular function, J. S. Carolina Med. Ass. **65**:26, 1969.

Mitchell, J., Sproule, B., and Chapman, C.: The physiological meaning of the maximal O_2 intake test, J. Clin. Invest. **37**:538, 1958.

Moody, D., Kollias, J., and Buskirk, E.: Evaluation of aerobic capacity in lean and obese women with four test procedures, J. Sports Med. **9**:1, 1969.

Ouellet, Y., Poh, S., and Becklake, M.: Circulatory factors limiting maximal aerobic exercise capacity, J. Appl. Physiol. **27**:874, 1969.

Pugh, L.: Athletes at altitude, J. Physiol. (London), **192**:616, 1967.

Robinson, S.: Experimental studies of physical fitness in relation to age, Int. Z. Angew. Physiol. **10**:251, 1938.

Shephard, R.: The relative merits of the step test, bicycle ergometer and treadmill in the assessment of cardio-respiratory fitness, Int. Z. Angew. Physiol. **23**:219, 1966.

Shephard, R.: Methodology of exercise tests in healthy subjects and in cardiac patients, Canad. Med. Ass. J. **99**:354, 1968.

Shephard, R., et al.: Standardization of submaximal exercise tests, Bull. WHO **38**:765, 1968.

Shephard, R., and Pelzer, A.: The working capacity of subjects from an exhibition crowd, Canad. Med. Ass. J. **94**:171, 1966.

Sjöstrand, T.: Changes in the respiratory organs of workmen at an ore smelting works, Acta Physiol. Scand. **196**:687, 1947.

Taylor, C.: Some properties of maximal and submaximal exercise with reference to physiological variation and measurement of exercise tolerance, Amer. J. Physiol. **142**: 200, 1944.

Taylor, H., Buskirk, E., and Henschel, A.: Maximal oxygen intake as an objective measure of cardiorespiratory performance, J. Appl. Physiol. **8:**73, 1955.

Tornvall, G.: Assessment of physical capabilities, Acta Physiol. Scand. **58:**201, 1963.

Truett, J., Benson, H., and Balke, B.: On the practicability of submaximal exercise testing, J. Chronic Dis. **19:**711, 1966.

Wyndham, C.: Submaximal tests for estimating maximum oxygen intake, Canad. Med. Ass. J. **96:**736, 1967.

Wyndham, C., et al.: Maximum oxygen intake and maximum heart rate during strenuous work, J. Appl. Physiol. **14:**927, 1959.

Wyndham, C., et al.: The influence of a stable diet and regular work on body weight and capacity for exercise in African mine recruits, Ergonomics **5:**435, 1962.

Wyndham, C., et al.: The influence of gross body weight on oxygen consumption and on physical working capacity of manual labourers, Ergonomics **6:**275, 1963.

Wyndham, C., et al.: Studies of the maximum capacity of men for physical effort, Int. Z. Angew. Physiol. **22:**285, 1966.

Wyndham, C., et al.: Improving the accuracy of prediction of an individual's maximum oxygen intake, Arbeitsphysiologie **23:**354, 1967.

Wyndham, C., et al.: Walk or jog for health, S. Afr. Med. J. **45:**53, 1971.

CHAPTER 18

ANAEROBIC CAPACITY

THEORY

Morehouse, L. E., and Miller, A. T., Jr.: Physiology of exercise, ed. 6, St. Louis, 1971, The C. V. Mosby Co., chaps. 2, 18, 24.

Åstrand, P.-O., and Rodahl, K.: Textbook of work physiology, New York, 1970, McGraw-Hill Book Co., chap. 9.

In very short but intensive muscular exertion, such as sprinting, endurance is limited by energy available from the splitting of the high-energy phosphate bond of adenosinetriphosphate (ATP) into adenosinediphosphate (ADP). This process is the anaerobic source of mechanical energy for muscular work and it is exhausted in a few seconds owing to its small capacity and high rate. The maximum anaerobic power that can be developed depends upon the content of ATP and its phosphate donor, creatine phosphate (CP), in the working muscles at the beginning of exercise and the speed of the splitting of these high-energy phosphates as determined by the enzymatic system in the muscles. Maximum anaerobic power is reached during the first 4 seconds of exercise at top speed. It remains constant for 4 to 6 seconds. After the sixth second the energy output declines steadily because of the decreased ATP and CP content in the working muscles. In this short time neither oxidative nor glycolytic processes take an appreciable part.

By performing an all-out exercise for only 3 to 5 seconds the maximum rate of work at highest intensity can be reached, and this is limited by the supply and the maximum rate of splitting of ATP and CP.

Exhaustion is not reached in this type of exercise, as it does not involve depletion of the alactic stores of energy, which requires 10 to 15 seconds of strenuous exercise.

If the incline of the ground is greater than 22%, the negative work of walking at the end of each step cycle is reduced to zero. The mechanical work performed in climbing is all positive work, given substantially by the body lift—that is, by the vertical component of the space covered. The vertical component of the speed in meters per second (m./sec.) indicates the mechanical power per kilogram of body weight (in kg.-m/kg./sec.).

Since the efficiency of this type of work is about 25%, the energy requirement per second (kcal./kg./sec.) can be calculated. This is the maximal anaerobic power. The maximal anaerobic power in normal fit young individuals is about 13 kcal./kg. per second. The total capacity of this energy source is only about 100 kcal. per kilogram.

COMPARISON WITH AEROBIC AND GLYCOLYTIC POWER

In contrast, the aerobic power (Chapter 17) amounts to about 3.6 kcal./kg. per second, while aerobic capacity is practically unlimited. The glycolytic emergency mechanism has a capacity of about 230 kcal. per kilogram and the power amounts to only 7 kcal./kg. per second. It is exhausted in less than 40 seconds during exercise at maximal intensity.

Athletic young men have highest maximal anaerobic power, and women, non-athletes, and older subjects show lower values. Little is known of the factors that influence anaerobic power.

LIMITATIONS

As in the case of aerobic power, anaerobic power is not directly indicative of the capacity to perform a particular exercise and tells nothing of the health of the subject.

METHOD (MARGARIA)

A convenient ergometric device for this kind of exercise is the climbing of a staircase at top speed, two steps at a time. The time taken to cover the distance from the second to the tenth step is measured in seconds. The acceleration at the start can be neglected; it occurs in the first step, prior to the time of measurement.

Equipment

- ☐ Ordinary staircase, a minimum of 10 steps high
- ☐ Electronic clock sensitive to 1/100 second, arranged to start when the subject's foot strikes the second step and to stop when the foot strikes the tenth step (photoelectric cells or microswitches)

Procedure

- ☐ Record body weight in kilograms.
- ☐ Measure the height of a stair riser in meters and multiply by 8 to determine the vertical lift.
- ☐ Measure the vertical lift between the second and the tenth step.
- ☐ Have subject run at top speed up the staircase, two steps at a time.
- ☐ Record the time in seconds taken to cover the distance between the second and the tenth step to obtain the time of travel.
- ☐ Compute W_v, the mechanical power (kg.-m./kg./sec.), by multiplying body weight in kilograms times the vertical lift in meters, dividing the sum by the body weight in kilograms, and dividing that result by the time of travel in seconds.

SAMPLE DATA SHEET

Body weight (kg.)	Vertical lift* (m.)	Time of travel (sec.)	Mechanical power (kg.-m./ kg./sec.)	Anaerobic power	
				$W_v \times \dfrac{100\dagger}{25}$ (kg.-m./kg./ sec.)	(kcal./ kg./hr.) ‡
75	1.224	0.816	1.5	6.0	50.63

*Vertical lift = riser height (0.153 m.) × number of steps (8).

$\dfrac{\dagger 100}{25} = \dfrac{\text{power input}}{\text{power output}} = 25\%$ efficiency.

‡To convert kg.-m. per second to kcal./kg. per second multiply by 0.002344. To convert kcal./kg. per second to kcal./kg. per hour multiply by 3600.

☐ Compute the anaerobic power (kg.-m./kg./sec.) by multiplying the mechanical power (W_v) by $\dfrac{100}{25}$, 25 being the percentage efficiency of this type of work.

☐ Convert the anaerobic power units (from kg.-m./kg./sec. to kcal./kg./hr.) by first multiplying by a factor of 0.002344 to convert kg.-m./kg./sec. to kcal./kg./sec. and then multiplying by 3600 (to convert kcal./kg./sec. to kcal./kg./hr.).

Proficiency check

Task	Date completed	Instructor's initials
1. Discuss the source of anaerobic power.		
2. Using the Margaria method, calculate the anaerobic power developed.		

Sample experiments

☐ Repeat anaerobic power runs after various rest intervals in an attempt to determine the time for restoration of energy sources.

☐ Relate anaerobic power to muscle mass.

☐ Study the effect of hyperthermia (heating) and hypothermia (cooling) on anaerobic power.

☐ Investigate the time period after starting the anaerobic power run in which the peak of power (fastest speed) is reached.

☐ Compare the aerobic power of the fastest and slowest starters in sprinting.

☐ Study the positive work required to meet wind resistance to progression and to accelerate the body at the start of a sprint race.

☐ Compare the energy cost of sprinting uphill on a treadmill (no wind resistance) with that of sprinting uphill on the ground at the same incline (with wind resistance). Caution: For this experiment the subjects should be sprint athletes trained to leap onto a fast-moving (11 m. per second) treadmill set at a 22% incline. A safety harness is necessary. During experimental conditions the subject should not grasp the handrail.

☐ Correlate anaerobic power with aerobic power (Chapter 17) in subjects with a wide range of fitness.

REFERENCE

Margaria, R., Cerretelli, P., Aghemo, P., and Sassi, G.: Energy cost of running, J. Appl. Physiol. **18:**367, 1963.

SUGGESTED READING

Margaria, R.: Anaerobic metabolism in muscle, Canad. Med. Ass. J. **96:**770, 1967.

Margaria, R.: Routine tests for aerobic and anaerobic muscular power. In Karvonen, M., and Barry, A., editors: Physical activity and the heart, Springfield, Ill., 1967, Charles C Thomas, Publisher.

Margaria, R.: Capacity and power of the energy processes in muscle activity: their practical relevance in athletics, Int. Z. Angew. Physiol. **25:**352, 1968.

Margaria, R.: An outline for setting significant tests of muscular performance, Milano, Instituto di Fisiologia Umana, Università di Milano.

Margaria, R., Aghemo, P., and Rovelli, E.: Measurement of muscular power (anaerobic) in man, J. Appl. Physiol. **21:**1662, 1966.

Margaria, R., et al.: Kinetics and mechanism of oxygen debt contraction in man, J. Appl. Physiol. **18:**371, 1963.

Margaria, R., Cerretelli, P., and Mangili, F.: Balance and kinetics of anaerobic energy release during strenuous exercise in man, J. Appl. Physiol. **19:**623, 1964.

Wyndham, C., et al.: Physiological requirements for world-class performances in endurance running, S. Afr. Med. J. **43:**996, 1969.

COMPUTER USAGE

Metabolic data collected during an ergometer test are reduced rapidly using an IBM 360/91 computer and a program* written in FORTRAN language. The data can be reduced and displayed almost instantaneously to the exercise test monitor using an interactive processor.

The following computer printout consists of seven sections. The first section at the top of the chart consists of a printout of the first job control card, which identifies the charge number.

The second section, identified by C's in the left columns, is a printout of comment cards that list the measurements from the exercise test.

The third section is a printout of the source deck. The source deck contains the FORTRAN language statements, which are translated into instructions to the computer as to the treatment of the metabolic and ergometric data.

The fourth section is a printout of the second job control card, which signifies the end of the above translation.

The fifth section is a printout of values of metabolic and ergometric data punched out on data cards. Labels are printed as instructed by certain cards in the source deck.

The sixth section is a printout of the results of the calculations performed by the computer. Labels are printed as instructed by cards in the source deck.

The seventh section is a printout of end of job information, showing computer time and storage area usage.

In preparing the program the following special procedures are used:

1. Data are punched on two cards; the first six items listed in the second section are punched on the first card in the order given, and the last seven items on the second card.

2. On the data cards, the first item of data is punched in decimal form in columns 1 through 10. For the second item, use 11 through 20, etc.

3. FORTRAN language statements in section three are punched starting in column 7 (one line per card).

4. Statement numbers (the four-digit numbers starting with 1000 in section three) are punched in columns 1 through 5.

5. Statement continuation numbers, opposite the blank spaces in the leftmost column in section three, are punched in column 6.

6. Prepare two data cards (one set of input data), with the first card punched VE = –10.0, and all five other items punched 0.0. On the second card punch all seven items 0.0. Place these at the end of the other data cards. These cause the computer to stop and thus terminate the running of the program.

---

*The program presented as an example was prepared by Jeff Johnson. The program was run at the U.C.L.A. Campus Computing Network facility.

```
*JOB    CC1780  JOHNSON                                                      WATFOR

        CCCCCC          CCCCCC            11        77777777    888888      000000
        CCCCCC          CCCCCCC           111       77777777    88888888    00000000
        CC              CC                111             77    88    88    00    00
        CC              CC                 11             77    888888      00    00
        CC              CC                 11            77     888888      00    00
        CC              CC                 11           77      88    88    00    00
        CCCCCCC         CCCCCCC          11111111      77       88888888    00000000
        CCCCCC          CCCCCC           11111111      77        888888      000000

C  INPUT DATA: VE IS VOLUME OF EXPIRED AIR MEASURED IN LITERS AT ATPS.
C  CT IS COLLECTION TIME MEASURED IN SECONDS.GMCORR IS THE CORRECTION
C  FACTOR FOR THE GASOMETER.TEMPC IS ROOM TEMPERATURE MEASURED IN DEGREES
C  CENTIGRADE,PB IS THE BAROMETRIC PRESSURE MEASURED IN MILLIMETERS OF
C  MERCURY,PH2O IS THE WATER VAPOR TENSION AT ROOM TEMPERATURE AS
C  MEASURED IN MILLIMETERS OF MERCURY. FIO2 IS THE PERCENT OF OXYGEN
C  INSPIRED AS EXPRESSED IN DECIMALS E.G. 22% = 0.22. FEO2 IS THE PERCENT
C  OF OXYGEN EXPIRED AS EXPRESSED IN DECIMAL FORM. FICO2 IS THE PERCENT
C  OFCARBON DIOXIDE INSPIRED AS EXPRESSED IN DECIMAL FORM. FECO2 IS THE
C  PERCENT OF CARBON DIOXIDE EXPIRED AS EXPRESSED IN DECIMAL FORM.BWT IS
C  THE SUBJECT'S BODY WEIGHT IN KILOGRAMS, HEART IS THE SUBJECT'S HEART
C  RATE DURING THE TEST RUN, ENGOUT IS THE WORK DONE PER MINUTE BY THE
C  SUBJECT AS MEASURED IN WATTS FROM THE ERGOMETER
        DATA NPRINT/6,NREAD/5/
        INDEX = 1
1000    READ(NREAD,1050) VE,CT,GMCORR,TEMPC,PB,PH2O,FIO2,FEO2,FICO2,
       1FECO2,BWT,HEART,ENGOUT
1050    FORMAT(6F10.5,7F10.5)
        IF(VE.LE.0.0) STOP
        WRITE(NPRINT,1100) INDEX
1100    FORMAT('1THE FOLLOWING OPEN CIRCUIT DATA WERE OBTAINED WITH THE'
       1' USE'/' OF THE BICYCLE ERGOMETER AS AN EXERCISE DEVICE'//'0TEST'
       2' RUN NUMBER',I6)
        WRITE(NPRINT,1150) VE,CT,GMCORR,TEMPC,PB,PH2O,FIO2,FEO2,FICO2,
       1FECO2,BWT,HEART,ENGOUT
1150    FORMAT(////' DATA USED IN THE ANALYSIS ARE AS FOLLOWS:'////' ',T10,
       1VE',T28,'CT',T46,'GMCORR',T63,'TEMPC',T82,'PB',T99,'PH2O'/' ',
       22X,'FIO2',5(6X,F12.5)/' ',T8,'FIO2',T26,'FECO2',T44,'FICO2',T62,
       3'FECO2',T79,'BWT',T96,'HEART',T114,'ENGOUT'/' ',F12.5,6(6X,F12.5))
        VEATPS=VE*60.0/CT*GMCORR
        WRITE(NPRINT,1200) VEATPS
1200    FORMAT(///'0',T17,'VOLUME EXPIRED ATPS =',F10.2,3X,
       1'LITERS PER MINUTE')
        VEBTPS=VEATPS*310.16/(273.16+TEMPC)*(PB-PH2O)/(PB-47.07)
        WRITE(NPRINT,1250) VEBTPS
1250    FORMAT('0',T17,'VOLUME EXPIRED BTPS =',F10.2,3X,
       1'LITERS PER MINUTE')
        VOBTPS=VEBTPS*(FIO2*(1.0-FECO2)-FEO2*(1.0-FICO2))/(1.0-FIO2-FICO2)
        WRITE(NPRINT,1300) VOBTPS
1300    FORMAT('0',T16,'OXYGEN UPTAKE BTPS =',F10.2,3X,
       1'LITERS PER MINUTE')
        VOSTPD=VOBTPS*273.16/310.16*(PB-47.07)/760.0
        WRITE(NPRINT,1350) VOSTPD
1350    FORMAT('0',T18,'OXYGEN UPTAKE STPD =',F10.2,3X,
       1'LITERS PER MINUTE')
        VOUNIT=VOSTPD*1000.0/BWT
        WRITE(NPRINT,1400) VOUNIT
1400    FORMAT('0','OXYGEN UPTAKE STPD PER UNIT WEIGHT =',F10.2,3X,
```

```
25          1'MILLILITERS PER KILOGRAM PER MINUTE')
26          VEUNIT=VEBTPS/BWT
27          WRITE (NPRINT,1450) VEUNIT
     1450   FORMAT('0',T4,'VENTILATION BTPS PER UNIT WEIGHT =',F10.2,3X,
           1'LITERS PER KILOGRAM PER MINUTE')
28          O2PUL=VOSTPD*1000.0/HEART
29          WRITE (NPRINT,1500) O2PUL
30   1500   FORMAT('0',T19,'OXYGEN PULSE STPD =',F10.2,3X,
           1'MILLILITERS PER MINUTE')
31          OPLBWT=O2PUL/BWT
32          WRITE (NPRINT,1550) OPLBWT
33   1550   FORMAT('0',T8,'OXYGEN PULSE PER UNIT WEIGHT =',F10.2,3X,
           1'MILLILITERS PER KILOGRAM')
34          VEQO2=VEBTPS/(VOSTPD*10.0)
35          WRITE (NPRINT,1600) VEQO2
36   1600   FORMAT('0',T14,'VENTILATION EQUIVALENT =',F10.2,3X,'LITERS')
37          RER=(FECO2*(1.0-FIO2)-FICO2*(1.0-FEO2))/
           1(FIO2*(1.0-FECO2)-FEO2*(1.0-FICO2))
38          WRITE (NPRINT,1650) RER
39   1650   FORMAT('0',T10,'RESPIRATORY EXCHANGE RATIO =',F10.2)
40          ENGYIN=348.583*VOSTPD
41          WRITE (NPRINT,1700) ENGYIN
42   1700   FORMAT('0',T3,'SUBJECT''S ENERGY USAGE PER MINUTE =',F10.2,3X,
           1'WATTS')
43          WRITE (NPRINT,1750) ENGOUT
44   1750   FORMAT ('0','SUBJECT''S ENERGY OUTPUT PER MINUTE =', F10.2, 3X,
           1'WATTS')
45          EFFICY=100.0*ENGOUT/ENGYIN
46          WRITE (NPRINT,1800) EFFICY
47   1800   FORMAT('0',T5,'SUBJECT''S PERCENT OF EFFICIENCY =',F10.2,3X,
           1'PERCENT')
48          INDEX = INDEX+1
49          GO TO 1000
50          END

     *RUN
```

THE FOLLOWING OPEN CIRCUIT DATA WERE OBTAINED WITH THE USE
OF THE BICYCLE ERGOMETER AS AN EXERCISE DEVICE

5

TEST RUN NUMBER   1

DATA USED IN THE ANALYSIS ARE AS FOLLOWS:

VE	CT	GMCORR	TEMPC	PB	PH2O
91.50000	66.00000	1.00000	23.00000	750.00000	21.0900

FIO2	FEO2	FICO2	FECO2	BWT	HEART	ENGOUT
0.2093	0.16601	0.00030	0.04310	75.00000	186.00000	180.00000

6

VOLUME EXPIRED ATPS   =   91.50   LITERS PER MINUTE

VOLUME EXPIRED BTPS   =   99.37   LITERS PER MINUTE

OXYGEN UPTAKE BTPS   =   4.30   LITERS PER MINUTE

OXYGEN UPTAKE STPD   =   3.51   LITERS PER MINUTE

OXYGEN UPTAKE STPD PER UNIT WEIGHT = 46.74   MILLILITERS PER KILOGRAM PER MINUTE

VENTILATION BTPS PER UNIT WEIGHT   =   1.32   LITERS PER KILOGRAM PER MINUTE

OXYGEN PULSE STPD   =   18.85   MILLILITERS PER MINUTE

OXYGEN PULSE PER UNIT WEIGHT =   0.25   MILLILITERS PER KILOGRAM

VENTILATION EQUIVALENT   =   2.83   LITERS

RESPIRATORY EXCHANGE RATIO   =   0.99

SUBJECT'S ENERGY USAGE PER MINUTE   = 1221.87   WATTS

SUBJECT'S ENERGY OUTPUT PER MINUTE = 180.00   WATTS

SUBJECT'S PERCENT OF EFFICIENCY   =   14.73   PERCENT

7

COMPILE TIME=   0.08 SEC,EXECUTION TIME=   0.01 SEC,OBJECT CODE=   3824 BYTES,ARRAY AREA=   0 BYTES,UNUSED=   149576 BYTES

Other computer programs related to exercise physiology are described in the following articles.

Kearney, J., and Stull, G.: A FORTRAN program for the reduction of open-circuit data, Res. Quart. Amer. Ass. Health Phys. Educ. **42**:223, 1971.

Laubach, L., and Marshall, M.: A computer program for calculating Parnell's anthropometric phenotype, J. Sports Med. **10:** 217, 1970.

Shephard, R.: Computer programs for solution of the Åstrand nomogram and the calculation of body surface area, J. Sports Med. **10**:206, 1970.

STANDARD UNITS* AND CONVERSIONS

INTERNATIONAL SYSTEM OF UNITS (SI)
Basic units

Unit	Symbol	Alternative symbols†
meter	m	m.
kilogram	kg	kg.
second	s	s., sec.
ampere	A	A.
degree Kelvin	K°	°K.
candela	cd	

Prefixes

deci-	means 10^{-1}	
centi-	means 10^{-2}	(e.g., 1 centimeter $= 10^{-2}$ meter)
milli-	means 10^{-3}	
deka-	means 10^{1}	
hecto-	means 10^{2}	
kilo-	means 10^{3}	

Derived units

Quantity	Name	Symbol	Alternative symbols
area	square meter	m^2	m.^{2}
volume	cubic meter or liter	m^3 or l	m.^{3}, L.
density	kilogram per cubic meter	kg/m^3	kg./m.^{3}
velocity	meter per second	m/s	m./sec.
force	newton	N (kg-m/s^2)	N (kg.-m./sec./ sec.)
pressure	newton per square meter (or mm. Hg)	N/m^2	N/m.^{2}
work ($=$ energy)	joule	J (N $\times$ m)	J (Nm.)
power	watt	w (J/s)	w. (J/sec.)

CONVERSIONS
Weight

Units are pound (lb.)
           kilogram (kg.)

To convert

lb.	to	kg.	multiply by	0.4536
kg.	to	lb.	multiply by	2.2046

---

*For standard symbols and units see Kaufman, W. C.: Standardization of symbols and units for environmental research, Physiologist **10**:89, 1967; also see Proposed standard system of symbols for thermal physiology, J. Appl. Physiol. **27**:439, 1969; and Standardization of definitions and symbols in respiratory physiology, Fed. Proc. **9**:602, 1950.

†Alternative symbols for standard units appear in some illustration labels and text discussion.

Length

Units are centimeter (cm.)
        meter (m.)
        kilometer (km.)
        inch (in.)
        foot (ft.)
        mile (mi.)

To convert

cm.	to	in.	multiply by	0.3937
cm.	to	ft.	multiply by	0.032808
m.	to	in.	multiply by	39.37
m.	to	ft.	multiply by	3.2808
km.	to	mi.	multiply by	0.62137
in.	to	cm.	multiply by	2.54
in.	to	m.	multiply by	0.0254
ft.	to	cm.	multiply by	30.48
ft.	to	m.	multiply by	0.3048
mi.	to	km.	multiply by	1.6093

Temperature

Units are degrees centigrade (°C.)
        degrees Fahrenheit (°F.)

To convert

°C.	to	°F.	$°F. = °C. \times (9/5) + 32$
°F.	to	°C.	$°C. = (°F. - 32) \times (5/9)$

Energy

Units are erg (E)
        joule (J)
        gram centimeter (gmcm)
        kilogram meter (kgm, kg.-m.)
        foot-pound (ftlb, ft.-lb.)
        kilocalorie (kcal or Cal, kcal. or Cal.)
        British thermal unit (BTU)

To convert

E	to	J	multiply by	10,000,000
E	to	gmcm	multiply by	0.00101989
J	to	gmcm	multiply by	1.01989
J	to	kgm	multiply by	0.101989
J	to	ftlb	multiply by	0.73801
J	to	kcal	multiply by	0.00023906
J	to	BTU	multiply by	0.00094787
gmcm	to	J	multiply by	0.00009805
gmcm	to	ftlb	multiply by	0.00007236
kgm	to	J	multiply by	9.805
kgm	to	ftlb	multiply by	7.236
kgm	to	kcal	multiply by	0.002344
kgm	to	BTU	multiply by	0.009298
ftlb	to	J	multiply by	1.3568
ftlb	to	gmcm	multiply by	13820
ftlb	to	kgm	multiply by	0.1382
ftlb	to	kcal	multiply by	0.000324
ftlb	to	BTU	multiply by	0.001286
kcal	to	J	multiply by	4183
kcal	to	kgm	multiply by	426.6
kcal	to	ftlb	multiply by	308.7

kcal	to	BTU	multiply by	3.9649
BTU	to	J	multiply by	1055
BTU	to	kgm	multiply by	107.52
BTU	to	ftlb	multiply by	778
BTU	to	kcal	multiply by	0.2522

Power

Units are watts (W)
horsepower (hp)
kilogram meters per second (kgm/s, kg.-m./sec.)
foot pounds per second (ftlb/s, ft.-lb./sec.)
British thermal units per second (BTU/s, BTU/sec.)
kilocalories per second (kcal/s, kcal./sec.)

To convert

W	to	hp	multiply by	0.00134
W	to	kgm/s	multiply by	0.101989
W	to	ftlb/s	multiply by	0.73801
W	to	BTU/s	multiply by	0.00094787
W	to	kcal/s	multiply by	0.0023905
hp	to	W	multiply by	745.96
hp	to	kgm/s	multiply by	76.04
hp	to	ftlb/s	multiply by	550
hp	to	BTU/s	multiply by	0.70707
hp	to	kcal/s	multiply by	0.1783
kgm/s	to	W	multiply by	9.8050
kgm/s	to	hp	multiply by	0.013151
kgm/s	to	ftlb/s	multiply by	7.236
kgm/s	to	BTU/s	multiply by	0.009298
kgm/s	to	kcal/s	multiply by	0.002344
ftlb/s	to	W	multiply by	1.3568
ftlb/s	to	hp	multiply by	0.0011818
ftlb/s	to	kgm/s	multiply by	0.1382
ftlb/s	to	BTU/s	multiply by	0.001286
ftlb/s	to	kcal/s	multiply by	0.000324
BTU/s	to	W	multiply by	1055
BTU/s	to	hp	multiply by	1.4143
BTU/s	to	kgm/s	multiply by	107.52
BTU/s	to	ftlb/s	multiply by	778
BTU/s	to	kcal/s	multiply by	0.2522
kcal/s	to	W	multiply by	4183
kcal/s	to	hp	multiply by	5.6085
kcal/s	to	kgm/s	multiply by	426.6
kcal/s	to	ftlb/s	multiply by	3087
kcal/s	to	BTU/s	multiply by	3.9649

Metabolic conversions

1 liter/min. $O_2 \approx$ 5 kcal./min. $=$ 20,913 joules/min. $=$ (20,913 $\div$ 60) joules/sec. $\approx$ 348.583 watts

1 BTU/sec. $=$ 1055 watts $=$ 3.027 liters/min. O_2

APPENDIX *C*

LIST OF EQUIPMENT COMMONLY USED IN PHYSIOLOGY OF EXERCISE LABORATORIES

- ☐ 0.5 ml. Scholander gas analyzer complete with reaction chambers, constant temperature bath, electric motor shaker, micrometer, pulley setup, burettes, belts, springs, transfer pipettes, leveling bulbs, syringe with bulbs, and acid reservoirs (Otto K. Hebel Scientific Instruments)
- ☐ Flexometer (Marxer Clinic, Santa Monica, California)
- ☐ Monark bicycle ergometer (Quinton Instruments)
- ☐ CardioPacer (Physiometrics, Inc.)
- ☐ Back and leg dynamometer, anthropometric tape, Lange skin-fold caliper, Jamar hand dynamometer (J. A. Preston Corp.)
- ☐ Baumanometer, V-lok cuff with Velcro (W. A. Baum Co.)
- ☐ Storage cabinet and wardrobe cabinet (All Steel Equipment Co.)
- ☐ Pedal model ergometer; total work integrator; cardiotachometric controller; automatic programmer; strip chart recorder; external instrument timer; remote tachometer; work load calibrator; cardiotach calibrator; 3-way valve; modified Otis-McKerrow valve; gas bag, Douglas type; rubber-tipped noseclips; rubber refills; mercury barometer; plastic tubing; molded rubber ends; cement, plastic to rubber; rubber mouthpieces; Collins blower motor with powerstat control; 350-liter gasometer (W. E. Collins)
- ☐ Gas analyzers (Beckman Instrument)
- ☐ Metronome with timer and automatic shutoff
- ☐ Wall clock with sweep-second hand (2)
- ☐ Stopwatch (4)
- ☐ Table fan, 6-inch blade, nonoscillating (2)
- ☐ Weights, 1, 2, 3, and 4 kg. (for calibrating bicycle ergometer)
- ☐ Tool kit—wrenches, screwdrivers, pliers (for adjusting equipment)
- ☐ Scales (Detecto-Medic)
- ☐ Stadiometer, wall-mounted
- ☐ Workbench
- ☐ Examining table, vinyl-covered padding (2)
- ☐ Biochemistry workbench supplied with water, compressed air, gas, and multiple electrical outlets
- ☐ Cabinet for storage (2)
- ☐ Glassware washing sink and cabinet
- ☐ Shower stall
- ☐ Furniture (desks, chairs, cabinets, etc.)

SOURCES OF MATERIALS

Abbeon, Inc., 179-22R Jamaica Ave., Jamaica, N. Y. 11432

Advanced Kinetics, 1231 Victoria St., Costa Mesa, Calif. 92627

AeroVac, Box 448, Troy, N. Y. 12181

AGAC Derritron, 1332 N. Henry St., Alexandria, Va. 22314

Air Control, 125 Noble St., Norristown, Pa. 19401

Aircraft Components, Inc., Benton Harbor, Mich.

Airpax Electronics, Box 8488, Ft. Lauderdale, Fla. 33310

Airsol Instruments, 26 Sparta Dr., Short Hills, N. J. 07078

Ajay Instruments, 31 Field St., Glenbrook, Conn. 06906

A. S. Aloe Co., 1150 S. Flower St., Los Angeles, Calif.

Alton Electronics, Box 185, Summit, N. J. 07901

American Chronoscope Corp., 216 W. 1st St., Mt. Vernon, N. Y.

American Electronic, Box 552, Lansdale, Pa. 19446

American Hospital Supply Corp., 2020 Ridge Ave., Evanston, Ill. 62205

American Meter Co., 13500 Philmont Ave., Philadelphia, Pa. 19116

American Optical Co., Box 361, Bedford, Mass. 01730

American Ultraviolet, 64 Commerce St., Chatham N. J. 07928

Ames Instruments, 1127 Myrtle St., Elkhart, Ind. 46514

Amlab, 1701 Elizabeth Ave., Rahway, N. J. 07065

Amprobe Instrument, 630 Merrick Rd., Lynbrook, N. Y. 11563

Amstro, 120 Clinton Rd., Fairfield, N. J. 07006

Ann Arbor Instrument Works, Inc., 1200 Rosewood St., Ann Arbor, Mich. 48104

API Instruments, 11655 Chillicothe Rd., Chesterland, Ohio 44026

Applied Research, Box 9406, Austin, Texas 78757

Aquarium Systems, 1450 E. 289th St., Wickliffe, Ohio 44090

Argonaut Associates, Box K, Beaverton, Ore. 97005

Arista Surgical Co., 67 Lexington Ave., New York, N. Y. 10010

Askania-Werke, 4913 Cordell Ave., Bethesda, Md. 20014

Associated Testing Labs, 162 Route 46, Wayne, N. J. 07470

Astro Mechanics, Box 9498-TR, Austin, Texas 78756

Atkins Technical, Box 14405, Gainesville, Fla. 32601

Atlas Electric Devices, 4114 N. Ravenswood, Chicago, Ill. 60613

Autotron, 3629 N. Vermillion St., Danville, Ill. 61832

Avionics Research Products, 6901 W. Imperial Hwy., Los Angeles, Calif. 90045

B & K Instruments, 5111 W. 164th St., Cleveland, Ohio 44142

BLH Electronics, 42 4th Ave., Waltham, Mass. 02154

BRS-Foringer, 5451 Holland Dr., Beltsville, Md. 20705

Bacharach Instrument, 625 Alpha Dr., Pittsburgh, Pa. 15238

Bailey Instruments, 5919 Massachusetts Ave., Washington, D. C. 20016

Balder Cryogenic, 26 Sparta Dr., Short Hills, N. J. 07078

Baldwin-Lima-Hamilton Corp., Waltham, Mass. 02154

Barnebey-Cheney, 835 N. Cassady Ave., Columbus, Ohio 43219

Barnes Engineering, 30 Commerce Rd., Stamford, Conn. 06902

Battle Creek Equipment Co., Battle Creek, Mich.

W. A. Baum, 620 Oak St., Copiague, N. Y. 11726

Bausch & Lomb Optical Co., Rochester, N. Y.

Beck Industries, Box 1679, Boulder, Colo. 80302

Beckman Instruments, 2500 Harbor Blvd., Fullerton, Calif. 92634

Beckman Spinco, 1117 California Ave., Palo Alto, Calif. 94304

Behavioral Controls, 1506 W. Pierce St., Milwaukee, Wis. 53246

Bel-Art Products, Pequannock, N. J. 07440

Belfort Instrument, 1600 S. Clinton St., Baltimore, Md. 21224

Bell Aerosystems, 4515 Superior Ave., Cleveland, Ohio 44103

Bell & Howell Co., 7100 McCormick Rd., Chicago, Ill.

Bendix-Scott Testers, 98 Blackstone, Providence, R. I. 02901

Benson-Lehrner Corp., 14761 Califa St., Van Nuys, Calif.

Bethesda Instrument, 4925 Fairmont Ave., Bethesda, Md. 20014

Biocom, 9522 W. Jefferson Blvd., Culver City, Calif. 90230

Bioelectronic Instruments, Box 204, Hastings-on-Hudson, N. Y. 10706

Bio-Medical Electronics, 653 Lofstrand Lane, Rockville, Md. 20850

Bioneers, Box 96, New Rochelle, N. Y. 10804

Biotronex Lab, 9153 Brookville Rd., Silver Spring, Md. 20910

Biotronics, Box 2987, Newport Beach, Calif.

Birtcher Corp., 4371 Valley Blvd., Los Angeles, Calif.

S. Blickman, 536 Gregory Ave., Weehawken, N. J. 07087

Brailsford & Co., Inc., Milton Point, Rye, N. Y.

Branson Instrument, 76 Progress Dr., Stamford, Conn. 06904

Brinkmann Instruments, Cantiague Rd., Westbury, N. Y. 11590

Brookline Instrument, 33 Virginia Rd., White Plains, N. Y. 10603

Burdick Corp., Milton, Wis.

Burklund Scientific, 919 N.Michigan, Chicago, Ill. 60611

G. F. Bush Associates, Box 175, Princeton, N. J. 08540

Bytrex, 223 Crescent St., Waltham, Mass. 02154

Cahn, 7500 Jefferson St., Paramount, Calif. 90723

Calbio Research, 12 Unami Lane, Scotch Plains, N. J. 07076

Calma, 707 Kifer Rd., Sunnyvale, Calif. 94086

Cambridge Instrument, 73 Spring St., Ossining, N. Y. 10562

Cardiac Electronics, 4915 Ransom Rd., Clarence, N. Y. 14031

Carey Scale, 714 Hamburg Tpk., Pompton Lakes, N. J.

Carle Instruments, 1141 E. Ash Ave., Fullerton, Calif. 92631

Carlson, 3457 Weidner Ave., Oceanside, N. Y. 11572

Carolina Medical Electronics, Box 307, King, N. C. 27021

Centorr Associates, Box 175, Suncook, N. H. 03275

Central Scientific Co., 2699 S. Kostner Ave., Chicago, Ill. 60623

Channel Industries, Box 3680, Santa Barbara, Calif. 93105

Charles Scientific, 295 Central Park West, New York, N. Y. 10024

Chemapec, 1 Newpark St., Hoboken, N. J. 07030

Chemical & Pharmaceutical, 260 W. Broadway, New York, N. Y. 10013

Chemtronics, Box 6996, San Antonio, Texas 78209

John Chatillon, 83-30 Kew Gardens Rd., Kew Gardens, N. Y. 11415

Cincinnati Sub-Zero Products, 2612 Gilbert Ave., Cincinnati, Ohio 45206

Clay-Adams, 299 Webro Rd., Parsippany, N. J. 07054

Colab Laboratories, 3 Science Rd., Glenwood, Ill. 60425

Coleman Instruments, Inc., 42 Madison St., Maywood, Ill.

W. E. Collins, 220 Wood Rd., Braintree, Mass. 02184

Colson Corp., Elyria, Ohio

Columbus Instrument, 1166 Chesapeake Ave., Columbus, Ohio 43212

Computer Instruments, 92 Madison Ave., Hempstead, N. Y. 11550

Computer Medical Science Corp., Box 1469, Conroe, Texas 77301

Comtel Corp., 1400 Holly Ave., Columbus, Ohio 43212

Conax, 2300 Walden Ave., Buffalo, N. Y. 14225

Conrac, 330 Madison Ave., New York, N. Y. 11017

Conrad-Missimer, Koch Rd., Corte Madera, Calif. 94925

Controlled Environments, 15 Stutsman St., Pembina, N. D. 58271

Cooke Vacuum, 13 Merritt St., South Norwalk, Conn. 06854

Cordis Corp., 241 N.E. 36th St., Miami, Fla.

Corning Glass Works, Lab Products, Corning, N. Y. 14830

Coulter Electronics, 590 W. 20th St., Hialeah, Fla. 33010

Curtin Scientific, Box 1546, Houston, Texas 77001

Custom Scientific Instrument, 13 Wing Dr., Whippany, N. J. 07981

Datametrics, 87 Beaver St., Waltham, Mass. 02154

Datascope, 520 Victor St., Saddle Brook, N. J. 07662

Davis Scientific, 11116 Cumpston, North Hollywood, Calif. 91601

Dekan Timing Device Co., Box 712, Glen Ellyn, Ill.

Del Electronic, 250 E. Sanford Blvd., Mt. Vernon, N. Y. 10550

Delta Scientific, 170 E. Hoffman Ave., Lindenhurst, N. Y. 11757

Denominator, Main St., Woodbury, Conn. 06798

Denoyer-Geppert, 5235 N. Ravenswood Ave., Chicago, Ill. 60640

Denton Vacuum, Cherry Hill Industrial Center, Cherry Hill, N. J. 08034

Detecto Scales, 540 Park Ave., Brooklyn, N. Y. 11205

W. C. Dillon, 14620 Keswick St., Van Nuys, Calif. 91407

DimcoGray Co., 207 E. 6th, Dayton, Ohio 45431

Disc Instruments, 2701 S. Halladay St., Santa Ana, Calif. 92705

Discon, 1150 N.W. 70th St., Ft. Lauderdale, Fla. 33309

M. Ducommun Co., 580 5th Ave., New York, N. Y. 10036

Dynasciences, 11661 San Vicente Blvd., Los Angeles, Calif. 90049

Dynisco, 20 Southwest Park, Westwood, Mass. 02090

E & M Instrument, Box 12511, Houston, Texas 77017

The Edin Co., Inc., 207 Main St., Worchester, Mass.

EG & G, Crosby Dr., Bedford, Mass. 01730

Eimer and Amend Lab Supplies, 633 Greenwich St., New York, N. Y. 11520

Electrodyne, Providence Hwy., Sharon, Mass. 02067

Electro-Medical Lab, Inc., South Woodstock, Vt.

Electronics for Life Sciences, Box 697, Rockville, Md. 20851

Electronics for Medicine, 30 Virginia Rd., White Plains, N. Y. 10603

Elema-Schonander, Siemens Medical of America, 60 W. Fay Ave., Addison, Ill. 60101

Elgin Exercise Appliance Co., Box 132, Elgin, Ill.

Endevco, 801 S. Arroyo Pkwy., Pasadena, Calif. 91109

Engis Equipment, 8035 Austin Ave., Morton Grove, Ill. 60053

Enraf-Nonius, 130 County Courthouse Rd., Garden City Park, N. Y. 10023

ENSCO, 3100 Eldredge St., Salt Lake City, Utah 84115

Environmental Growth Chambers, Box 407, Chagrin Falls, Ohio 44022

Esterline Angus, Box 24000, Indianapolis, Ind. 46224

Ets Bettendorff, S. A., 44 Rue de la Senne, Bruxelles, Belgium

Evans International, 72 Tanner, Haddonfield, N. J. 08033

Exact Weight Scale, 1005 W. 3rd Ave., Columbus, Ohio 43212

Fairchild Space & Defense, 300 Robbins Lane, Syosset, N. Y. 11791

Farrand Optical, 535 S. 5th Ave., Mt. Vernon, N. Y. 10550

Fenwal, 400 Main St., Ashland, Mass. 01721

Field Emission, Box 58, McMinnville, Ore. 97128

Fish-Schurman, 70 Portman Rd., New Rochelle, N. Y. 10820

Fisher Scientific, 711 Forbes Ave., Pittsburgh, Pa. 15219

Fiske Associates, Quaker Hwy., Uxbridge, Mass. 01569

Flexi-Optics Lab, 117 Dover St., Somerville, Mass. 02144

Flight Research, Box 1-F, Richmond, Va. 23201

Forma Scientific, Box 469, Marietta, Ohio 45750

Foto-Mem, 2 Mercer Rd., Natick, Mass. 07160

Franz Mfg. Co., Printers Lane, S. Blvd. Business Park, New Haven, Conn. 06519

The Garrett Corp., 9851 Sepulveda Blvd., Los Angeles, Calif.

A. E. Gay, R.D. 4 Chestnut Ridge, Lockport, N. Y. 14094

Genisco Technology, 18435 Susana Rd., Compton, Calif. 90221

Gentran, 2961 Corvin Dr., Santa Clara, Calif. 95051

Geoscience Nuclear, 2335A Whitney Ave., Hamden, Conn. 06518

Ralph Gerbrands, 8 Beck Rd., Arlington, Mass. 02174

Germfree Laboratories, 2600 S.W. 28th Lane, Miami, Fla. 33133

V. R. Gersmehl, 3817 Warren Ave., Cheyenne, Wyo.

Gilford Instrument Laboratories, Inc., Elyria, Ohio

Gilliland Instrument Co., 3124 E. 14th St., Oakland, Calif.

Gilson Medical Electronic, Box 27, Middleton, Wis. 53562

GM Mfg & Instrument, 3417 3rd Ave., Bronx, N. Y. 10451

Goerz Optical, 461 Doughty Blvd., Inwood, N. Y. 11696

Grason Stadler, 56 Winthrop St., W. Concord, Mass. 07181

Grass Instrument, 101 Old Colony Ave., Quincy, Mass. 02169

H. J. Green Instruments, 2500 Shames Dr., Westbury, N. Y. 11590

Greiner Scientific, 20 N. Moore St., New York, N. Y. 10013

Guenberg Electronics, 585 Gregory Ave., Weehawken, N. J. 07087

Gulton Industries, Metuchen, N. Y. 08840

W. & L. E. Gurley, 514 Fulton St., Troy, N. Y. 12181

Hale-Reaction Performance Timer, Box 1127, Williamsport, Pa. 17701

Hamilton Mfg., 1316 18th St., Two Rivers, Wis. 54241

Hamilton Standard, Box 1000, Windsor Locks, Conn. 06096

Harford Metal Products, Bldg. 101, Aberdeen, Md. 21001

Harvard Apparatus, 150 Dover Rd., Millis, Mass. 02054

Harvard Instrument Co., Dover, Mass.

Heath Co., Hilltop Rd., Benton Harbor, Mich. 49022

Heathkit Co., Benton Harbor, Mich. 49022

Otto K. Hebel, Scientific Instruments, 80 Swarthmore Ave., Rutledge, Pa.

Heusser Instrument, 121 W. Malvern Ave., Salt Lake City, Utah 84115

Hewlett-Packard, 1501 Page Mill Rd., Palo Alto, Calif. 94304

High Accuracy Productions, 141 Spring St., Claremont, Calif. 91711

High Temperature, 225 W. Lehigh Ave., Philadelphia, Pa. 19133

High Vacuum Equipment, 2 Churchill Rd., Higham, Mass. 02043

E. Vernon Hill, Box 14248, San Francisco, Calif. 94114

S. Himmelstein, 2500 Estes Ave., Elk Grove Village, Ill. 60007

Hoffrel Instrument, Moody's Lane, Norwalk, Conn. 06851

Honeywell, 4800 E. Dry Creek Rd., Denver, Colo. 80217

Hotpack, 5086A Cottam Ave., Philadelphia, Pa. 19135

Hudson Photographic, Irvington-on-Hudson, N. Y. 10533

Hughes Aircraft, Centinela & Teale, Culver City, Calif. 90230

Hunter Mfg. Co., Inc., Quarry Rd., Coralville, Iowa

Hydro-Tex Corp., 939 W. Wilson Ave., Chicago, Ill.

Hygrodynamics, 949 Selim Rd., Silver Spring, Md. 20910

Iconix, 1175 O'Brien Dr., Menlo Park, Calif. 94025

Information International, 12435 W. Olympic Blvd., Los Angeles, Calif. 90064

Instron, 2500 Washington St., Canton, Mass. 02021

Instrumentation Associates, Inc., 17 W. 60th St., New York, N. Y. 10023

Instrumentation Lab, 113 Hartwell Ave., Lexington, Mass. 02173

Instrumentation Marketing Corp., 820 S. Mariposa St., Burbank, Calif. 91506

International Applied Science, 510 S. Franklin St. Hempstead, N. Y. 15550

International Transducer, Box 3385, Santa Barbara, Calif. 93105

Itek, 10 Maguire Rd., Lexington, Mass. 02173

Ithaco, 735 W. Clinton St., Ithaca, N. Y. 14850

James Instrument, 26 Sparta Dr., Short Hills, N. J. 07078

Jarrell-Ash, 590 Lincoln St., Waltham, Mass. 02154

Jewel Aquarium, 5005 W. Armitage Ave., Chicago, Ill. 60639

Jones Medical Instrument Corp., 315-321 S. Honore St., Chicago, Ill. 60612

Jordan Scientific Products, 2200 Kennedy St., Philadelphia, Pa. 19137

Kahl Scientific Instrument, 737 Main, El Cajon, Calif. 92022

Kaman Nuclear, 1700 Garden of Gods Rd., Colorado Springs, Colo. 80907

Keleket/CGR, 1603 Trapelo Rd., Waltham, Mass. 02154

Kenelco, Inc., 1753 Cloverfield Blvd., Santa Monica, Calif.

Keuffel & Esser Co., 500 Central, Northfield, Chicago, Ill.

Kimble Productions, Box 1035, Toledo, Ohio 43601

Kimray, Inc., 52 N.W. 42nd St., Oklahoma City, Okla.

Kinney Vacuum, 3529 Washington St., Boston, Mass. 02130

Kistler Instrument, 8989 Sheridan Dr., Clarence, N. Y. 14031

Kontes Glass, Spruce St., Vineland, N. J. 08360

David Kopf Instruments, Box 636, Tujunga, Calif. 91042

LKB Instruments, 12221 Parklawn Dr., Rockville, Md. 20852

L-W Photo, 15451 Cabrito Rd., Van Nuys, Calif. 91406

LabConCo Corp., 8810 Prospect, Kansas City, Mo. 64132

LaBerne Mfg. Co., Box 254, Columbia, S. C.

Lab-Line Instruments, Lab-Line Plaza, Melrose Park, Ill. 60160

Lafayette Instrument Co., N. 26th St. & 52 Bypass, Lafayette, Ind.

LaMotte Chemical Products, Chestertown, Md. 21620

LaPine Scientific, 6001 S. Know Ave., Chicago, Ill. 60652

Lee Scientific, 18 Washington Ave., Chelsea, Mass. 02150

Leeds & Northrup, Sumneytown Pike, North Wales, Pa. 19454

Lehigh Valley Electronic, Box 125, Fogelsville, Pa. 18051

Leighton Flexometer, Inc., 1351 E. 55th Ave., Spokane, Wash.

Lexington Instruments, 241 Crescent St., Waltham, Mass. 02154

Lightning-Lite Co., 14414 Detroit Ave., Lakewood, Ohio

Ling Electronics, 1515 S. Manchester Ave., Anaheim, Calif. 92803

Loenco, 1062 Linda Vista, Mountain View, Calif. 94040

London, 811 Sharon Dr., Cleveland, Ohio 44145

Theodore M. Long Engineering Specialties, 40 S. Bridge St., Somerville, N. J.

Luft Instruments, Old Winter St., Lincoln, Mass. 01773

Macbeth, Box 950, Newburgh, N. Y. 12550

Maclevy Products Corp., 320 5th Ave., New York, N. Y. 10001

Magnaflux, 7300 W. Lawrence Ave., Chicago, Ill. 60656

David W. Mann, 174 Middlesex Tpk., Burlington, Mass. 01803

Marietta Apparatus, 118 Maple St., Marietta, Ohio 45750

Maroth Engineering Co., Wilton, Conn. 06897

Marquette Electronics, 3712 W. Elm St., Milwaukee, Wis. 53209

Massey Dickinson, 9 Elm St., Saxonville, Mass. 01701

MB Electronics, Box 1825, New Haven, Conn. 06508

McKesson Appliance Co., 2228 Ashland Ave., Toledo, Ohio

M. D. Electronics, 2415 N. Parish Place, Burbank, Calif.

Measurement Science, Box 338, Brigham City, Utah 84302

Measurement Systems, 523 West Ave., Norwalk, Conn. 06850

Medaids, 373 Dawson Dr., Camarillo, Calif. 93010

Medical Equipment Co., 1036 N.E. 6th Ave., Portland, Ore.

Medical Systems, 230 Middle Neck Rd., Great Neck, N. Y. 11021

Medicon, 2800 N. Figueroa St., Los Angeles, Calif.

Meditron Co., 708 S. Fair Oaks Ave., Pasadena, Calif.

Med-Science Electronics, 2647 Locust St., St. Louis, Mo. 63103

Medtronic, 3055 Old Hwy. 8, Minneapolis, Minn. 55418

Mettler Instrument, 20 Nassau St., Princeton, N. J. 08540

Meylan Stopwatch Co., 264 W. 40th St., New York, N. Y. 10018

Micron Instruments, 1519 Pontius Ave., Los Angeles, Calif. 90025

Milhard Engineering Co., 13619 Saticoy St., Van Nuys, Calif. 91402

Minco Products, 7300 Commerce Lane, Minneapolis, Minn. 55432

Mitchell Camera, 666 W. Harvard St., Glendale, Calif. 91209

MKS Instruments, 45 Middlesex Tpk., Burlington, Mass. 01803

Moeller Instrument, Box 8, Richmond Hill, N. Y. 11418

H. E. Morse Co., 455 Douglas Ave., Holland, Mich.

MSA Research, Evans City, Pa. 16033

Naniloa, 1118 N. Reynolds Rd., Toledo, Ohio 43615

Narragansett Gynmastics Equipment Co., 110 W. Carpenter St., Moberly, Mo.

National Instrument Labs, 12300 Parklawn Dr., Rockville, Md. 20852

Nebraska Medical Instruments, 6018 Oak St., Omaha, Neb. 68106

Newark Pedometer Co., 95 Monroe St., Newark, N. J. 07105

Newport Laboratories, Box 2087, Newport Beach, Calif.

Niessen-Medart Co., 3535 DeKalb St., St. Louis, Mo.

Non-Linear Systems, Box N, Delmar, Calif. 92014

Northeast Instrument, 91 Keiber Ct., Staten Island, N. Y. 10314

Nuclear Chicago, 2000 Nuclear Dr., Des Plaines, Ill. 60018

Nucleonic Corporation of America, 810 Williams Ave., Brooklyn, N. Y. 11207

Ohaus Scale, 29 Hanover Rd., Florham Park, N. J. 07932

Ohio Medical Products, 1400 E. Washington Ave., Madison, Wis. 53701

Optical Electronics, Box 11140, Tucson, Ariz. 85706

Optometric Instruments, 111 N. La Cienega, Beverly Hills, Calif. 90211

Orion Research, 11 Blackstone St., Cambridge, Mass. 02139

Oxygen Equipment & Service, 8335 S. Halsted, Chicago, Ill. 60620

Pacific Scientific Co., 6280 Chalet Dr., Bell Gardens, Calif.

Pacific Transducer, 2301 Federal Ave., Los Angeles, Calif. 90064

Parke-Davis, Medical Instruments Division, 223 Crescent St., Waltham, Mass. 02154

Parks Electronics Lab, 12770 S.W. 1st St., Beaverton, Ore., 97005

Parr Instrument, 211 53rd St., Moline, Ill. 61265

Particle Data, Box 265, Elmhurst, Ill., 60126

Peel-A-Way Scientific, 1800 Floradale, South El Monte, Calif. 91733

Pennsylvania Electronics Technology, 1397 Frey Rd., Pittsburgh, Pa. 15235

Pennsylvania Scale, 21 Graybill Rd., Leola, Pa. 17540

Percival Refrigeration, 1440 Walnut, Des Moines, Iowa 50309

Perkin-Elmer, 916 Meridian Ave., South Pasadena, Calif. 91030

Philips Electronic, 750 S. Fulton Ave., Mt. Vernon, N. Y. 10550

Phipps & Bird, 303 S. 6th St., Richmond, Va. 23205

Phoenix Precision Instrument, 3803 N. 5th St., Philadelphia, Pa. 19140

Photo Kinetics, 1624 Stillwell Ave., Bronx, N. Y. 10461

Photobell, 12 E. 22nd St., New York, N. Y. 10010

Physiometrics, Inc., 27727 Pacific Coast Hwy., Malibu, Calif. 90265

Picker Nuclear, 1275 Mamaroneck Ave., White Plains, N. Y. 10605

Polyfoam Packers, 6415 N. California Ave., Chicago, Ill. 60645

Polymetric, 1415 Park Ave., Hoboken, N. J. 07030

Polysciences, Paul Valley, Warrington, Pa. 18976

Polzer, John O., 4739 N. 19th St., Milwaukee, Wis.

Porto-Clinic Instruments, Inc., 298 Broadway, New York, N. Y.

Powers Regulator, 3400 Oakton St., Skoki, Ill. 60076

Precision Scientific Co., 3737 W. Cortland St., Chicago, Ill.

J. A. Preston Corp., 71 5th Ave., New York, N. Y. 10003

Proper Mfg., 10-34 44th Dr., Long Island City, N. Y. 11101

Quinton Instruments, 3051 44th Ave. W., Seattle, Wash. 98199

Jules Racine, 521 5th Ave., New York, N. Y. 10017

Radiation Equipment, 26 Sparta Dr. Short Hills, N. J. 07078

Radiation Facilities, 63 Dell Glen Ave., Lodi, N. J. 07644

Remex Electronics, 5250 W. El Segundo, Hawthorne, Calif. 90250

Research Media, 163 Eileen Way, Syosset, N. Y. 11791

RFL Industries, 215 Powerville Rd., Boonton, N. J. 07005

Richardson Camera Co., 2201 W. Desert Cove, Phoenix, Ariz.

Rustrak Instrument, Municipal Airport, Manchester, N. H. 03103

Sage Instruments, 230 Ferris Ave., White Plains, N. Y. 10603

Sanborn Co., 172 Wyman St., Waltham, Mass.

Sargent-Welch, 4647 Foster Ave., Chicago, Ill. 60630

August Sauter, 80 5th Ave., New York, N. Y. 10011

Scheer Instrument, 26 Sparta Dr., Short Hills, N. J. 07078

Schoeffel Instrument, 24 Booker St., Westwood, N. J. 07675

Schuco, 110 5th Ave., New York, N. Y. 10011

Schultz Instruments, Box 13385, Gainesville, Fla. 32601

Science Guides, 11 W. 42nd St., New York, N. Y. 10036

Scientific Advances, 1400 Holly Ave., Columbus, Ohio 43212

Scientific Glass Apparatus, 735 Broad, Bloomfield, N. J. 07003

Scientific Industries, 55 Madison Ave., Hempstead, N. Y. 11550

Scientific Notebook Co., 719 Wisconsin Ave., Oak Park, Ill.

Scientific Prototype, 615 W. 131st St., New York, N. Y. 10027

Scientific Research Instruments, 6707 Whitestone Rd., Baltimore, Md.

Scientific Supplies, 3950 N.W. Yeon, Portland, Ore.

Searle/BMI, 1220 10th St., Berkeley, Calif. 94710

Seattle Artificial Kidney, 3401 17th Ave. W., Seattle, Wash. 98119

Sela Electronics, 545 W. End Ave., New York, N. Y. 10024

Servonic Instruments, 1644 Whittier Ave., Costa Mesa, Calif. 92627

Sherer-Gillett, S. Kalamazoo Ave., Marshall, Mich. 49068

Sherwood Medical Industries, Inc., 1831 Olive St., St. Louis, Mo. 63103

Sidam, 107 Washington St., New York, N. Y. 10006

Siemens Medical of America, 60 W. Fay Ave., Addison, Ill. 60101

Sigma Instruments, 170 Pearl St., Braintree, Mass. 02185

Sigma Motor, 3 N. Main St., Middleport, N. Y. 14105

Signatron, 17124 S. Western Ave., Gardena, Calif. 90247

Simpson Electric, 5200 W. Kinzie St., Chicago, Ill. 60644

Singer, 1077 E. Arques Ave., Sunnyvale, Calif. 94086

Sloan Instruments, Box 4608, Santa Barbara, Calif. 93103

Southfield Electronic, 21250 Civic Center Dr., Southfield, Mich. 48075

Space/Defense, 1600 N. Woodward Ave., Birmingham, Mich. 48011

Sparton Southwest, 9621 Coors Rd. N.W., Albuquerque, N. M. 87103

W. F. Sprengnether Instrument, 4567 Swan Ave., St. Louis, Mo. 63110

Statham Instrument, 2230 Statham Blvd., Oxnard, Calif. 93030

C. H. Stoelting, 424 N. Homan Ave., Chicago, Ill. 60624

Sunbeam Technology, 50 Middlesex Tpk., Bedford, Mass. 01730

Syd Meadows Physical Fitness Co., 2460 Warrensville Rd., Cleveland, Ohio

Systems Research & Development, 4083 Glencoe St., Venice, Calif. 90291

Systron-Donner, 1 Systron Dr., Concord, Calif. 94520

Takeikiki Kogyo Co., Toyko, Japan

Taylor Instrument Co., 95 Ames St., Rochester, N. Y. 14601

Teca, 220 Ferris Ave., White Plains, N. Y. 10603

Technical Instruments, 441 Washington Ave., North Haven, Conn. 06473

Technical Operations, South Ave., Burlington, Mass. 01803

The Technicon Cardiograph Corp., 215 E. 149th St., New York, N. Y.

Technicon Cybex, Inc., Tarrytown, N. Y. 10591

Techni-Tool, 1216 Arch. St., Philadelphia, Pa. 19107

Technology/Versatronics, 506 S. High, Yellow Springs, Ohio 45387

Tektronix, Box 500, Beaverton, Ore. 97005

Teledyne/Geotech, Box 1650, Pasadena, Calif. 91109

Tenney Engineering, 1090 Springfield Rd., Union, N. J. 07083

Tensitron, Box 185, Cambridge, Mass. 01451

Testing Machines, 400 Bayview Ave., Amityville, N. Y. 11701

Texas Instruments, Inc., 13500 N. Central Expressway, Dallas, Texas

Thermal Research, Florence Ave. and Broadway, Union Beach, N. J. 07735

Thermo Electric, 109 5th St., Saddle Brook, N. J. 07662

Thermo-Lab Instruments, 1308 Route 8, Glenshaw, Pa. 15116

Thermonetics, Box 9112, San Diego, Calif. 91209

Thermotron, 937 S. Washington Ave., Holland, Mich. 49423

Thermovac Industries, 41 Decker St., Copiague, N. Y. 11726

Theta Instrument, 22 Spielman Rd., Fairfield, N. J. 07006

Arthur H. Thomas, Vine St. & 3rd, Philadelphia, Pa. 19105

Thwing-Albert, 10960 Dutton Rd., Philadelphia, Pa. 19154

Toledo Scale Co., Toledo, Ohio

Torsion Balance, 35 Monhegan St., Clifton, N. J. 07013

Tracor, 6500 Tracor Lane, Austin, Texas 78721

Traid, 777 Flower St., Glendale, Calif. 91201

Tri-R Instruments, 48 Merrick Rd., Rockville Centre, N. Y. 11570

United Systems, 918 Woodley Rd., Dayton, Ohio 45403

United Technical, Bradford St., West Concord, Mass. 01781

Vanguard Instrument Corp., 20 W. Centennial Ave., Roosevelt, N. Y.

Varian, 611 Hansen Way, Palo Alto, Calif. 94303

Veeder-Root, 70 Sargeant St., Hartford, Conn. 06102

Victory Engineering, Box 187, Springfield, N. J. 07081

Vidar, 77 Ortega Ave., Mountain View, Calif. 94040

VirTis, Rt. 208, Gardiner, N. Y. 12525

W. J. Voit Rubber Co., 315 E. Grand Ave., Chicago, Ill.

Waters Co., 2411 7th Ave., N.W., Rochester, Minn. 55901

WeatherMeasure, Box 41257, Sacramento, Calif. 95841

Webb Associates, 27727 Pacific Coast Hwy., Malibu, Calif. 90265

Weksler Instruments, 80 Mill Rd., Freeport, N. Y. 11520

West Instrument, 3860 N. River Rd., Schiller Park, Ill. 60176

Westinghouse Electronic, Box 2278, Pittsburgh, Pa. 15230

David Wexler & Co., 1243 S. Wabash Ave., Chicago, Ill.

Robert E. White Instruments, 33 Commercial Wharf, Boston, Mass. 02110

Will Scientific, 39 Russell St., Rochester, N. Y. 14603

Wolff, 2485 Huntington Dr., San Marino, Calif. 91108

W-P Instruments, 2822 State St., Hamden, Conn., 06517

Yellow Springs Instrument Co., Box 279, Yellow Springs, Ohio 45387

A. R. Young Co., 520 N. Dorman St., Indianapolis, Ind.

The Zimmer Mfg. Co., Warsaw, Ind.

LIST OF PERIODICALS REPORTING NEW EXERCISE PHYSIOLOGY INSTRUMENTATION

Biomedical News, Biomedical News Publishing Co., Inc., 5611 Columbia Pike, Falls Church, Va. 22041

Bel-Arts Products, Bolab, Inc., 359 Main St., Reading, Mass. 08167

Developments, Cole-Parmer Instrument Co., 7425 N. Oak Park Ave., Chicago, Ill. 60648

Guide to Scientific Instruments, American Association for the Advancement of Science, 1515 Massachusetts Ave., N.W., Washington, D. C. 20005

Instrument & Apparatus News, 845 Ridge Ave., Pittsburgh, Pa.

Lab Apparatus, The Chemical Rubber Co., 18901 Cranwood Parkway, Cleveland, Ohio 44128

The Lab Mart, J. & H. Berge, Inc., 4111 S. Clinton Ave., South Plainfield, N. J. 07080

Laboratory Management, Media Horizons, Inc., 200 Madison Ave., New York, N. Y. 10016

Laboratory Supply News, Laboratory Supplies Co., Inc., 29 Jefry Lane, Hicksville, N. Y. 11801

Medical Electronics News, 845 Ridge Ave., Pittsburgh, Pa.

Medical Equipment, 28 Craven St., London, WC2N 5PD, England

Medical Research Engineering, Medical-Research-Technology, Woods Rd., Great Notch, Little Falls, N. J. 07424

Plastic Ware, Cole-Parmer Instrument Co., 7425 N. Oak Park Ave., Chicago, Ill. 60648

Product Guide, Ivan Sorvall, Inc., Norwalk, Conn. 06856

Products for Science, Cole-Parmer Instrument Co., 7425 N. Oak Park Ave., Chicago, Ill. 60648

Scientific Review, The Chemical Rubber Co., 18901 Cranwood Parkway, Cleveland, Ohio 44128

Sources of Equipment for Sports Science Laboratories, Physical Efficiency Laboratory of the University of Geulph, Ontario, Canada

Sources of Research Laboratory Equipment, Res. Quart. Amer. Ass. Health Phys. Educ. **40:**651, 1969.

INDEX